Vision

e first year of
ature"

1994

Contents

Foreword

"I am delighted to receive this unique report from the Chief Nursing
Officer on progress in nursing, midwifery and health visiting since
"A Vision for the Future" was launched a year ago. It is a great
achievement by any standards and I want to congratulate the
professions for the advances they have made in the development
of professional practice and the delivery of high quality patient care."

Julia Cumberlege

Baroness Cumberlege
PARLIAMENTARY UNDER SECRETARY OF STATE
DEPARTMENT OF HEALTH

" The report which follows, while it focuses on nursing, midwifery
and health visiting contributions to health care, is about the core
business of the National Health Service. I am impressed by the
energy and commitment the professions have given to this task
and want to ensure that general managers, doctors and other
colleagues continue to collaborate with them in the programme
of work which the Chief Nursing Officer sets out. I recommend
the report to chief executives and others not only because it
informs them about progress which has already been made; but
also to seek their active support in forwarding the programme
in the next and subsequent years."

Alan Langlands

Alan Langlands
CHIEF EXECUTIVE
NHS EXECUTIVE

" I want to thank all those nurses, midwives and health visitors who
have helped the nursing directorate of the National Health Service
Executive compile this report. The findings are a celebration of what
the professions have done to ensure that the care that patients and
clients receive is sensitive to their needs and sensitively given by a
named nurse throughout their period of care. That care is based on
sound practice backed up by research where this is available; and,
the outcomes known and submitted to clinical audit. I know that the
professions will be keen to work with me in the future to
consolidate the gains which have been made."

Yvonne Moores

Yvonne Moores
CHIEF NURSING OFFICER/DIRECTOR OF NURSING
NHS EXECUTIVE

Executive Summary

The monitoring exercise shows an encouraging response to the "Vision for the Future" targets for 1993/94, particularly those concerned with individualised nursing and midwifery care, clinical practice and research and the development of outcome indicators. The exercise shows that:

- 95% of units have developed a system to monitor the named nurse initiative;

- 96% of units were confident that nurses could identify the caseload of patients for whom they were responsible;

- 93% of units had identified at least one outcome indicator responsive to nursing, midwifery and health visiting care; and 83% had developed clinical protocols to support this.

- 95% of units had established local networks to disseminate good practice based on research;

- 86% of units had changed areas of clinical practice as a result of research findings;

- more work is required to ensure that "Vision" targets become part of the corporate agenda and local business plans;

- the professions' input into purchasing needs to be better understood and developed;

- developments in the five key areas should be consolidated and the twelve targets retained for further progress and be monitored in the next and following years.

Future work should focus first, on consolidating broad achievements in detail. To encourage this the report recommends that the professions retain the five key areas in the "Vision for the Future" and that they follow up and develop the targets within it. Secondly, they should implement policy initiatives of relevance to nursing and midwifery which have arisen since the "Vision" was launched.

To help the professions to do this the Chief Nursing Officer intends to hold a series of workshops with nurse executives of trusts to gain their views on the next steps to be taken in each of the targets; and, their views on how new policy initiatives should be absorbed within the nursing, midwifery and health visiting agenda. This will result in a publication later in the year. The exact nature, focus and timing of the next monitoring exercise will be decided as a result of discussions between the Chief Nursing Officer, the Executive Board and the professions.

I
Introduction

This report describes progress in implementing "A Vision for the Future" launched by the Secretary of State in April 1993. It describes broad national trends and identifies areas and targets with which the professions have had most success and those which have been more challenging. A way forward for the future is outlined.

BACKGROUND

"A Vision For The Future" arose after wide consultation with the nursing professions. It outlines the contribution of the nursing professions to health and health care and describes good practice in five key areas. The key areas are quality, outcomes and audit; accountability for practice; clinical and professional leadership and clinical supervision; purchasing and education.

Measurable objectives to be met in the first year were built into the twelve targets associated with each of these areas. The Department of Health's nursing, midwifery and health visiting resources have supported and evaluated progress against these objectives in collaboration with various parts of the National Health Service over the last year. The progress report which follows is based on the monitoring, evaluation and reporting arrangements agreed by the Secretary of State and the Chief Executive of the National Health Service Executive.

II
Monitoring, Evaluation and Reporting Arrangements

The Nursing Directorate's plan of action included:

- a communication and dissemination programme with discussions and presentations to regional nursing officers, the Standing Nursing Midwifery Advisory Committee (SNMAC), trust nurse executives and in conferences and workshops.

- a steering group with members drawn from each part of the National Health Service and SNMAC which was set up to advise on the implementation programme;

- development of a monitoring questionnaire, piloted, adjusted and agreed with the implementation steering group, the results of which inform this report.

- the development of guidance on target nine on purchasing and target ten on clinical supervision.

METHOD

A monitoring questionnaire was designed, agreed with the implementation steering group, and piloted amongst trust nurse executives. The pilot led to some additional questions being included so the pilot results were not used with the main survey results. The modified questionnaire was printed to a high standard in booklet form and sent under cover of a letter from the Chief Nursing Officer. While not intended as a full audit of the entire population the survey response rate was sufficient to say that, at a 95% confidence level, the true results are no more than ±3% from those quoted in the text.

A total of 669 questionnaires were mailed to the NHS. They were primarily aimed at directors of nursing and trust nurse executives but the sample population also included regional nurse officers, purchasing nurses and nurse advisors. The questionnaires were distributed on 24th December 1993 and the respondents given until 4th February 1994 to respond.

Returned questionnaires were screened for completeness and consistency. A database was designed and constructed using SmartWareII. The data was input by members of an external data processing agency, and random spot checks were made to ensure accuracy. The data respondents provided was of high quality, and many respondents reinforced their answers with a wealth of supporting material. There was a good spread of responses between specialities, a good split of respondents across "waves" of trusts, annual budget size; and number of nurses, health visitors and midwives employed in the unit.

There were some 292 operational trusts in the first, second and third waves and 135 directly managed units which had achieved trust status in shadow form during the period of the study.

Of the 427 questionnaires distributed to hospital and community provider units a total of 260 were returned - a response rate of over 60%. In established trusts the response rate was much higher at 74%. This is a remarkably high response rate not only because completing the questionnaire was voluntary; but it was time consuming during a period when many units were actively preparing for trust status and the roles of chief officers, including nurses, were evolving. The respondents were normally the director of nursing, nurse manager, nurse advisor, chief nurse or the equivalent in the unit.

The usual qualifications about the nature of data collected by means of a national survey apply to this as other surveys of its kind. The questionnaire measures the responses of individuals to particular questions. It cannot, and does not seek to describe the complete range and quality of the actions which underlie the responses to the questions.

Table 1: Response rate

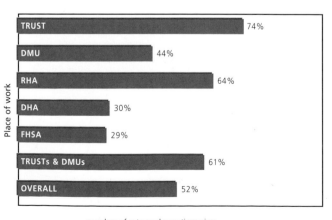

$$\text{Response rate} = \frac{\text{number of returned questionnaires}}{\text{number mailed out}}$$

III
Findings

The findings are presented as broad national trends in progress in each of the targets in the "Vision". As the targets were mainly concerned with delivery of care, provider units are the focus of the analysis which follows. Where a target is mainly addressed to a purchasing authority, a regional health authority, or, the nursing directorate of the Department of Health, this is recognised and acknowledged in the analysis of results. The term "respondents" usually refers to those questionnaires returned from trusts or DMUs unless specified otherwise.

GENERAL

It was important to establish whether all nurses, midwives and health visitors as well as nurse executive directors knew about the "Vision".

Nearly all units (95%) reported that the nurses, midwives and health visitors in their unit had seen a copy and discussed the "Vision". Over a third (37%) had attended a workshop or conference on the subject.

It was equally important to discover the extent to which the "Vision" had been discussed more widely in the unit. The news on this was positive, 59% of units reported that "A Vision for the Future" had been discussed with their board.

THE TWELVE TARGETS

This section reports on each of the twelve targets.

◎ Target One

Each patient client should have been assigned to a named nurse, midwife or health visitor throughout their period of care and local units will be expected to have developed the means of monitoring the named nurse, midwife and health visitor initiative.

It is encouraging to see that nearly all (95%) units reported they will have a means of monitoring the named nurse, midwife and health visiting initiative in the first year. However, while the systems to monitor the initiatives are in place it is important not to underestimate the time that it takes to ensure that it is fully implemented throughout a trust. Shifts in attitude and cultural changes take time, and some trusts and directly managed units (DMUs) will need to consider the results of monitoring to remedy any shortfalls found.

Target Two

A consumer satisfaction survey on the quality of the partnership and users involvement in care should have been completed and the findings conveyed to the nurses, midwives and health visitors concerned.

A majority (81%) of the respondents will have completed a consumer satisfaction survey and conveyed the findings to the staff concerned by April 1994. The method of doing this included staff meetings (73%) and distributing reports (61%). Many of the respondents enclosed copies of their surveys with the questionnaire. Other methods included quarterly quality reviews and team briefings. The use of consumer satisfaction surveys have been found to be a valuable source of information on users views of the service and those trusts /DMUs who have not achieved this target will no doubt wish to do so in the next year.

Table 2: Means of Conveying Information

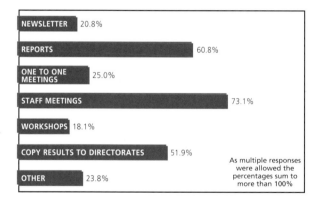

 Target Three

All provider units should have identified three outcome indicators responsive to nursing, midwifery and health visiting practice; developed relevant clinical protocols and have in place, as part of the management organisation, a framework of clinical audit to establish baseline data against which local targets can be set for the future.

Developing methods of care which are based on an understanding of a desired outcome and identifying indicators which will demonstrate that the desired outcome has been achieved is a very challenging task. Nearly all respondents have responded to the challenge.

93% had identified at least one outcome indicator and a large number (83%) stated that clinical protocols to support outcome indicators would be developed by the end of the first year. A significant number (79%) reported that a framework of clinical audit for at least one of the outcome indicators identified will be in place by April 1994.

This was a considerable achievement. It involved people thinking about their current practice and making judgements about whether it could be improved by an approach based on measuring the outcomes of care.

The range of outcome indicators, some of which are multidisciplinary, deserve special mention and demonstrate that the professions are playing a very important part with their clinical colleagues in developing an approach which stresses outcomes for patients rather than inputs by professionals.

The most common outcome indicators cited were prevalence of pressure sores, hospital acquired infection rates, wound and leg ulcer healing rates and maintenance of eye and oral hygiene. In the care of the mentally ill, the elderly, those with diabetes and in some surgical units, the length of stay, and reduction in readmission rates were featured. Similarly, reduction in reported levels of pain, reduction in disturbed behaviour, reduction of levels of anti-depressants or sedatives were all seen as pertinent outcome indicators.

In the community the percentage of babies breast fed at three months, the percentage of children who had pre-school boosters and the percentage of babies who had been vaccinated with the new HIB vaccine were studied. One unit had looked at the percentage of children with learning disabilities who are continent at 7 years, another at the success of enuresis treatment.

District health authorities and regional health authorities were also interested in developing information on outcomes and in helping to train nurses and members of professions allied to medicine in the use of outcome indicators.

Target Four

Purchasers and providers should be able to demonstrate that they are including value for money recommendations in their contracts for services.

Generally, value for money initiatives were seen as part of the larger corporate agenda. However, many of the respondents (69%) were able to describe value for money or Audit Commission recommendations related to nursing and midwifery which could be found in contracts for service. The Audit Commission reports quoted as the source of value for money initiatives included "Virtue of Patients", "Homeward Bound", "Lying in Wait", and "Children First".

It was reported by many that contracts required information on staffing establishment by skill mix and qualification. This information was often based on teamwork demand methodology found in the nurse management information system.

Several units had undertaken nursing staff activity analysis which had led to relocating services. For example, all high dependency care to one ward or unit; the reduction of shift overlap; shift pattern changes; and more focused bed management. Various types of work profile analysis and work load dependency studies have been undertaken.

 Target Five

Clinical and professional leaders should have taken steps to discuss with each nurse, midwife and health visitor how they might develop their practice.

At the end of the first year, most (96%) report that steps will have been taken to discuss with nurses and midwives how they might develop their practice. Of course in many units clinical and professional leaders other than the nurse executive director will have held these discussions with individual members of staff.

Most commonly, individual performance review (84%), and a personal development plan (79%) were used. Other steps included the use of profiles or portfolios; training needs analysis; supervision and appraisal. This was clearly an area of great interest and importance to all nurses and midwives at each level in a trust.

◎ **Target Six**

*Each nurse, midwife and health visitor should be able to
clearly identify the caseload or group of patients/clients for
whom he/she is the named professional and for whom he/she
bears a responsibility for care.*

Nearly all (96%) respondents were confident that each nurse,
midwife and health visitor could identify the caseload of
patients for whom they were responsible.

◎ **Target Seven**

*Employing authorities will need to demonstrate what action
they have taken to identify and support those with potential to
develop leadership and management skills*

Potential leadership and management skills will have been
identified by 93% of units by the end of the first year. Most
frequently, candidates are selected for management training,
given time off to study or had been delegated specific project
work. Other common methods included attendance at
managerial/professional development programmes, involvement
in succession planning programmes, allowing for periods of
acting up, or undertaking study programmes (MBA or in-house).

Table 3: Developing the potential of those identified

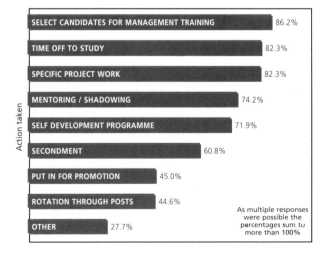

Target Eight

Professional leaders should be able to demonstrate the existence of local networks to disseminate good practice based on research.

Networks to disseminate practice based on local and/or national research findings have been established by 95% of units. Meetings, professional advisory groups and the circulation of papers were the most usual form of networking but journal clubs, practice committee/groups, research groups have also been set up.

This finding and the one that follows is very encouraging in that it links with earlier results on the development of clinical outcomes. It demonstrates an impressive trend towards basing nursing practice on sound research; identifying outcomes and evaluating practice as part of clinical audit.

Table 4: Networks Disseminating Good Practice Based on Research

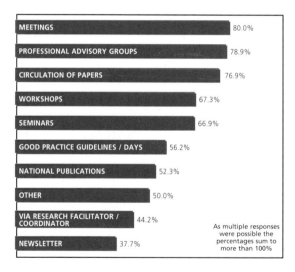

MEETINGS	80.0%
PROFESSIONAL ADVISORY GROUPS	78.9%
CIRCULATION OF PAPERS	76.9%
WORKSHOPS	67.3%
SEMINARS	66.9%
GOOD PRACTICE GUIDELINES / DAYS	56.2%
NATIONAL PUBLICATIONS	52.3%
OTHER	50.0%
VIA RESEARCH FACILITATOR / COORDINATOR	44.2%
NEWSLETTER	37.7%

As multiple responses were possible the percentages sum to more than 100%

 Target Nine

Providers should be able to demonstrate at least three areas where clinical practice has changed as a result of research findings.

Nurses and midwives are interested in research. Many (86%) stated that areas of clinical practice will have changed in their unit as a result of research findings. The range of nursing care influenced by research was impressive especially, as some respondents noted, because it involves a major shift in approach. Many nurses and midwives are clearly prepared to examine what they do, and why, and to use research to question and, if necessary, change practice.

Examples quoted included reconsidering pressure area care and care of leg ulcers; advice for mothers on education in relation to preventing cot death; management of potential suicides; handling challenging behaviour; management of pain, and many others.

Target Ten

Discussions should be held at local and national level on the range and appropriateness of models of clinical supervision and a report made available to the professions.

Discussions on clinical supervision in nursing and health visiting have been held in many (86%) units. As part of the nursing directorate's commitment to the target the Chief Nursing Officer wrote to the professions in February of this year (CNO PL 94(5)), commending a report by Faugiere and Butterworth as a means of forwarding discussions with the professions, the UKCC, the ENB and professional organisations.

Target Eleven

Good practice from leading edge purchasing authorities demonstrating the input of nursing, midwifery and health visiting advice should be drawn together and shared with other purchasing authorities.

89% of those purchasing authorities who responded stated that nursing advice had been drawn together and shared with other purchasers. However, it is disappointing to note that the response rate to the questionnaire by purchasers was lower than that for provider units, about one third of whom felt that sharing of input had not occurred .

This is a newly emerging area for all participants in health care and one which will clearly need attention in the future. The study commissioned by the Department of Health on the contribution of nurses, midwives and health visitors to purchasing, together with the good practice examples which it describes, will help to do this. It is to be published later this year.

⊚ **Target Twelve**

Each provider unit should be able to identify particular pre and post registration programmes planned to help nurses, midwives and health visitors acquire the necessary skills associated with the Health of the Nation, Caring for People, and the Patients Charter/Named Nurse initiative.

More than three quarters of respondents identified education and training programmes planned to help staff to acquire skills associated with "Health of the Nation" ,"Caring for People" and the "Patients Charter/Named Nurse" initiative. These programmes were listed in some detail and ranged from formal ENB courses (eg. ENB 934 Care and Management of Individuals with HIV and AIDS) to seminars, workshops, awareness programmes and interdisciplinary multi-agency training with local authorities and others. (For example; child protection, working with older people, assessment).

Table 5: Education Programmes

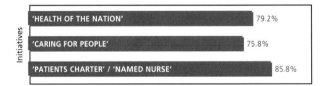

Initiatives	
'HEALTH OF THE NATION'	79.2%
'CARING FOR PEOPLE'	75.8%
'PATIENTS CHARTER' / 'NAMED NURSE'	85.8%

VIEWS ABOUT THE VISION

There were a series of open ended questions seeking views about the "Vision" and how it should be moved forward locally and nationally. Generally, respondents were optimistic about what they might do in the future although they did report some difficulties in implementing the "Vision" in the first year. These were as follows:

Organisational Difficulties

Several people spoke about the difficulty of implementing the "Vision" when there was turbulence in an organisation. As reorganisations and structural changes occurred, the "Vision" was seen to be a low priority or one which was difficult to place on the corporate agenda. Some people thought translating the language of nursing in a multidisciplinary culture was difficult. Others noted the difficulty that members of the professions had in finding time out to consider the implications of the "Vision" when other priorities competed for their attention.

Substantive Difficulties

One view suggested that the "Vision" provided too huge and challenging an agenda to meet within the timescale given.

Conceptual Difficulties

Others considered that tighter definitions of the terms found in "A Vision" would have helped.

Future Local Intentions

Units were asked what direction they intended to take in the future. Many respondents spoke of incorporating "Vision" targets into local strategies and implementation programmes or expanding them into new areas, for example, night duty. Others intended to use "Vision" principles as a common organisational objective for all professionals and to formally monitor the results. Many respondents intended to develop one or more targets further, for example outcome indicators and research based practice.

Some units with internal service agreements and business plans will seek to insure that "Vision" objectives form part of these plans. Many units plan to run workshops, open learning packages, or away days to raise the profile of the "Vision" locally. Others will develop a local monitoring mechanism over specified timescales. Generally the "Vision" is seen as the baseline upon which nursing, midwifery and health visiting can be developed; or, which supports pre-existing business plans.

Future at National Level

Respondents were asked what direction "Vision" should take in the future at national level. The majority view was that consolidation of the areas and targets for one further year should take place, after which achievements should again be monitored. Most considered that the results of the monitoring exercise should be shared with the NHS and that the "Vision" should be given a high profile nationally. A significant number considered the "Vision" should be incorporated into corporate contract objectives and monitored in the second and subsequent years.

IV
Summary

"A Vision for the Future" was based on a wide ranging consultation exercise and reflects the views of the professions on best practice in nursing, midwifery and health visiting. The five key areas and the twelve targets were selected because they captured those views. Some trusts and directly managed units had already taken steps to develop clinical practice and organise care in the ways described in the "Vision". For them, there was less work to do. Some had developed one or more of the targets but not all of them. Others had yet to develop strategies of nursing and midwifery with measurable objectives or targets.

The monitoring exercise showed that the timing and publication of the "Vision" was helpful not only to those who were just developing a programme, but also to those who were further along the road. It was valued because it raised the profile of the professions and their contribution to the corporate agenda, and because it provided a blueprint upon which local objectives might be based.

The findings confirm that nurses, midwives and health visitors in the National Health Service have either already developed or have begun to develop systems and made advances in all of the five key areas identified in the "Vision for the Future". Some targets, particularly one, five, six, seven, eight, have been implemented by nearly all respondents. These targets were concerned with:

● setting up systems to monitor the named nurse/midwife initiative;

● holding discussions with individual nurses and midwives on developing their practice;

● feeling confident that the patients for whom individuals were responsible for care could be identified.

Setting up systems which focus on individualised care for patients is demonstrably part of the mainstream agenda. Units are also actively seeking to support those with leadership potential and were able to demonstrate the existence of local networks to disseminate good practice based on research.

An impressive majority reported that they had met targets two, three nine, ten and twelve. These targets were concerned with:

● developing consumer satisfaction surveys

● identifying outcome indicators

● changing practice as a result of research

● discussing clinical supervision

● providing education and training

It is important not to underestimate the challenge associated with changing the basis on which care is delivered so that practice is based on sound research and its outcomes charted and evaluated by means of audit. That so many units had begun this process of questioning, changing attitudes, culture, and clinical activity is reassuring. Advanced practice can be found in community nursing, mental health nursing, and all types of acute and rehabilitative care. Those who have not yet tackled these targets will want to do so and those who have already done so be encouraged to expand the areas involved. The good news is one of steady achievement in some very demanding objectives.

The two remaining targets, four and eleven, concerned with:–

● using value for money recommendations in contracts;

● sharing good practice in nursing, midwifery and health visiting input to purchasing;

– have been achieved by fewer units and authorities. This is not surprising. Expertise in purchasing and contracting is a new area for the professions and one with which they will need increasingly to be involved.

Overall, targets with a quite specific professional and clinical focus; whether concerned with providing individualised nursing care, developing professional practice, using research or the newly emerging area of clinical outcomes, have captured the imagination and energetic attention of the professions. However, some reported that it was less easy to capture the attention of the multidisciplinary team in a turbulent and changing environment, despite the fact that the nursing contribution is so vital to delivering the corporate agenda.

Life does not stand still and new policy initiatives have been introduced since the "Vision for the Future" was published in 1993. They will need to be absorbed within the nursing and midwifery programmes. Some of the policy initiatives are more complex than others. They involve change in clinical practice and the organisational and professional cultures in which care takes place. Many of these changes have been welcomed by the professions, in alliance with patients, clients and others, for example "Changing Childbirth", "Working in Partnership: A Collaborative Approach to Care", "Ethnic Minority Staff in the NHS: A Programme of Action." All of them will take place in a larger organisation which is itself altering in shape.

The contribution of nurses and midwives to these initiatives and the corporate objectives of the NHS, will need to be absorbed into the "Vision" agenda.

V
The Way Forward

The response to the targets for 1993/94 is very encouraging, but it is clear that not all units will be ready to move on to a different set of targets nor should they be expected to do so. Rather, future work should concentrate on consolidating broad achievements; and developing practice in each target; as well as incorporating new policy initiatives.

The monitoring exercise was itself seen as helpful in focusing attention on the nursing and midwifery agenda and the majority of those who responded to it considered it should be repeated in some form after the second and third years.

In order to help the professions to consolidate and develop their achievements the Chief Nursing Officer intends to hold a series of workshops with nurse executives of trusts to gain their views on the next steps to be taken in each of the targets; and, their views on how new policy initiatives should be absorbed within the nursing, midwifery and health visiting agenda. This will result in a publication later in the year. The exact nature, focus and timing of the next monitoring exercise will be decided as a result of the discussions between the Chief Nursing Officer, the Executive Board and the professions.

References

"A Vision for the Future":
DH NHSME April 1993

"The A to Z of Quality":
NHSME September 1993

"Changing Childbirth":
HMSO 1994

"Ethnic Minority Staff in the NHS":
NHSME 1994

"Public Health: Responsibility of the NHS and the Roles of Others"
HSG (93) 56. DH 1993

"Working in Partnership: A Collaborative Approach to Care"
DH March 1994

Further copies

Further copies of this report and "A Vision for the Future"
can be obtained by writing to:

BAPS
Health Publications Unit
DSS Distribution Centre
Heywood Stores
Manchester Road
Heywood
Lancashire
OL10 2PZ

U213

International Development:
Challenges for a World in Transition

Introduction to

POVERTY and INEQUALITY

Prepared for the Course Team by Judith Scott

Cover photo Landless Brazilian peasants, members of Movimento Sem Terra, demonstrating for more equal land distribution.

The Open University
Walton Hall
Milton Keynes
MK7 6AA
United Kingdom

First published 2001

Edited, designed and typeset by The Open University

Printed in the United Kingdom by The Alden Group, Oxford

ISBN 0 7492 3809 7

This publication forms part of an Open University course U213 *International Development: Challenges for a World in Transition*

Details of this and other Open University courses can be obtained from the Call Centre, PO Box 724, The Open University, Milton Keynes, MK7 6ZS, United Kingdom, tel. +44 (0)1908 653231, email ces-gen@open.ac.uk. Alternatively, you may visit the Open University website at http://www.open.ac.uk where you can learn more about the wide range of courses and packs offered at all levels by the Open University

If you have not already enrolled on the course and would like to purchase this or other Open University material, contact Open University Worldwide Ltd, The Berrill Building, Walton Hall, Milton Keynes MK7 6AA, United Kingdom: tel. +44 (0)1908 858785; fax +44 (0)1908 858787; email ouwenq@open.ac.uk; website http://www.ouw.co.uk

1.1

Contents

Theme Introductions

Poverty and Inequality is one of the five Themes you will cover whilst studying this course. The other four Themes are: *Transitions*, *Technology and Knowledge*, *Displacement*, *Sustainability*.

Five weeks of study are set aside during Part 1 of U213 for these Theme Introductions, each comprising one week. You are expected to study them after you have completed your study of *Poverty and Development into the 21st Century* (Allen and Thomas, 2000; hereafter called the Course Book) and its associated audiocassettes, as directed by *Study Guide 1*. At the end of this five-week period a further week is set aside for you to complete tutor-marked assignment TMA 03 and to make your Theme choices for Part 2 of the course.

Remember that in Part 2 you will study *three* of the five Themes in the following order:

> *Transitions* (compulsory Theme)
>
> *Poverty and Inequality* or *Technology and Knowledge*
>
> *Displacement* or *Sustainability*.

The final section of *Study Guide 1* provides information that should help you make your choices. You should return to this once you have completed your study of the Theme Introductions.

Even if you are already certain which Themes you intend to study in Part 2 you should study all five Introductions in Part 1, including this one. This is because each Introduction practises skills that are relevant to other Themes; also we expect you to obtain a rounded view before you specialize. You may be assessed in your final examination on the learning outcomes associated with any of the Introductions. You will also be encouraged to illustrate TMA 03 with examples from a range of the Themes.

The Theme Introductions are self-contained, although, as noted above, they all assume that you have completed your study of the Course Book and its associated audiocassettes. We recommend, however, that you study them during this five-week period in the following order:

First week	*Transitions*
Second week	*Poverty and Inequality*
Third week	*Technology and Knowledge*
Fourth week	*Displacement*
Fifth week	*Sustainability*

The sixth week has been set aside for completing TMA 03 and making your choices for Part 2 of the course.

Studying *Introduction to Poverty and Inequality*

Some general aims of this Introduction are presented below. We also provide a checklist of learning outcomes. These are what we expect you to be able to do once you have completed the Introduction and are what you are potentially assessed upon in your TMAs and/or final examination.

The main text contains activities for you to undertake. These are included to engage you *actively* with the text and to foster deeper-level study than you will be able to achieve simply by reading. Typically these activities check that you understand what is being written and can critically engage with it, and draw you into the process of developing the text argument. Do therefore attempt to do the activities before reading the comments that follow them. The main text also directs you from time to time to the Course Book, so make sure that you always have this to hand.

You should aim to complete studying this text in one week (about 12–14 hours of study time) which means that you should think of ways to divide up your time to work through this material. This will naturally vary between students depending on when you have time available to work and how quickly you can go through the material.

Aims

The aims of this Introduction are to:
- draw out the multifaceted aspects of poverty in the Course Book;
- encourage you to think critically about poverty and inequality;
- provide a bridging link from Part 1 of the course for those who want to study the *Poverty and Inequality* Theme in Part 2.

Learning outcomes

Having studied this Introduction, you should be able to do the following:

1 Understand different conceptualizations of poverty and inequality.

2 Understand the multidimensionality, complexity and interrelated causes and effects of poverty.

3 Locate poverty and inequality in the local and global processes discussed in the Course Book and the Study Guide for Part 1.

4 Distinguish between poverty and inequality and understand how they are related.

5 Use concepts of poverty and inequality to analyse examples of deprivation.

6 Understand how different policy proposals on poverty and inequality are related to different views of development.

7 Handle data on poverty (simple calculations and critical interpretation).

8 Handle data on inequality both within and between countries.

1 About this Theme

You are probably doing this course partly because you are concerned about social injustice and interested in what can be done about poverty. Having read *Poverty and Development into the 21st Century*, you have already read quite a lot about poverty and inequality but you might not have had time to give these concepts much thought. The aim of this Introduction, therefore, is to help you think more carefully and critically about them but with an important purpose: to equip you with the ability to evaluate proposals for tackling poverty.

We start in Section 2 by discussing the fundamental question of *why* poverty matters and to whom. This is to get us thinking about the breadth of the topic before we start looking at different conceptions of poverty in Section 3. These are vital foundation stones because poverty can mean many things, and how we conceptualize poverty affects how we analyse it (Section 4) and measure it (Section 5). For example, someone who defines poverty as 'low income' will explore and measure different factors from someone who regards poverty as, say, 'powerlessness'. And, in turn, seeing poverty in terms of low income is likely to produce rather different policies from those based on viewing poverty as powerlessness. In other words, policies are not simply technical solutions: they are essentially political decisions reflecting different conceptualizations not only of poverty but of social justice. Social justice refers to how we think goods and rewards should be distributed within and between societies. So in Section 6 there are some important philosophical ideas about inequality and social justice and how they relate to poverty.

By the time we reach our final Section 7, then, we shall be better equipped to think about one of the central questions underlying the course: 'what can be done about poverty?' (Course Book, pp.4–5). There are no easy answers to this and the section doesn't seek to provide any. Rather, it tries to show how we can use our understanding, built up in the previous sections, to think critically about poverty programmes and policies. Policy processes aimed at tackling poverty at various levels from the household to the international will be explored in far greater depth in Part 2 of the course but Section 7 will, I hope, be stimulating and useful whether or not you are pursuing the *Poverty and Inequality* Theme any further.

Before we get going, I just want to draw your attention to two general points:

First, you will notice that much of the theoretical discussion in this Introduction draws on the work of Amartya Sen. You have come across some of his ideas already in the Course Book, notably poverty as a failure of capabilities (Chapter 1) and the concepts of endowments and entitlements (Chapter 3). Sen is a Nobel prize-winning economist and philosopher whose work on poverty and inequality has been (and continues to be) very influential, not only among academics in the development field but, increasingly, in fora such as the United Nations Development Programme and the World Bank whose policies will be discussed in detail in Part 2.

Secondly, poverty can be analysed and tackled at various levels, from individuals, households and small communities to national and international levels. We shall be employing all these levels at various points in this Introduction. It is important to be able to recognize them and to understand that they are linked. For example, national policies such as tax structures and social security systems will have an impact on poverty at the individual and household levels. The national impact may complement or contradict attempts to alleviate poverty at these other levels but the effect will also vary according to the wide variety of situations faced by different individuals, households and communities. The following extract provides an example of different levels interacting.

> Following a complaint by the US that the EU's banana import regime unfairly favoured Europe's former colonies and discriminated against other producers, such as Latin American countries where US companies produce bananas, the WTO [World Trade Organization] ordered the EU to change aspects of its import regime. Last month EU ministers agreed rules which eliminated the licensing system that the US said was unfair. However, the EU maintained an import quota on Latin American bananas and a duty-free access quota which benefits Caribbean and other traditional exporters. …
>
> Caribbean producers account for 3 per cent of world banana exports, and 20 per cent of EU imports, says the Caribbean Banana Exporters Association. Dominica, St. Lucia and St. Vincent depend on banana exports for about 60 per cent of their export earnings. But production costs in the islands from small farms on hilly terrain are higher than those in the large plantations in Latin America. Caribbean exporters say the EU regime is necessary for their survival because they could not compete in the open market. 'Generations of farmers and entire families in these islands have been weaned on bananas, and they know nothing else. And we would not know where to start with marketing anything else.'
>
> (James, 1998)

This example demonstrates how action at the international level (the WTO and US government in conflict with the EU) has a direct effect on the livelihoods of small-scale farmers in the Caribbean who have to compete on the world market with US companies who produce bananas on large plantations in Latin America. The Caribbean producers have their own Association but it clearly needs EU support against the powerful combination of the WTO, the US government and transnational corporations (TNCs) in the banana trade. So we can only begin to understand economic problems facing small communities and households in the Caribbean by analysing their relationships to larger institutions.

2 Why does poverty matter?

Let's start by thinking about a very basic question: why does poverty matter and to whom? We can analyse *why* poverty matters in terms of moral, socio-economic and political issues and we can also ask *to whom* it matters at different levels, e.g. individuals, households, governments, private companies, the World Bank and so on.

For example, poverty might matter in an *economic* sense because it could be a constraint on economic growth. Whatever the nature of the economic system (capitalist, socialist, subsistence), impoverished people tend to be inefficient producers due to illness and lack of food, education, technology and other resources. This doesn't mean that poor people don't work hard; on the contrary, as Wield and Chataway (Course Book, p.121) make clear, they often work extremely hard. The problem is that their labour productivity is low.* This means that huge amounts of work are done without contributing to economic growth. And if economic growth is low, alternative employment opportunities will also be very limited.

*To remind yourself of the concept of labour productivity see the Course Book, p.113.

Poor people make poor consumers so they cannot provide much of a market for goods produced by other sectors of the economy. This also constrains economic growth.

Economically poor societies cannot easily get investment in productive enterprises nor in the infrastructure necessary to boost their productive capacities. The infrastructure required is both physical (e.g. transport systems, communications, energy, water) and social (e.g. health, education, markets, financial and legal systems).

But who might be concerned about these economic constraints? At one level, the output and earnings of individuals and households will be adversely affected by low labour productivity and unemployment and their consumption of goods and services will be restricted. Unemployment, in turn, has a profound effect on people's well-being, not only in material terms but in the effects of poor health, depression, stress, isolation and low self-esteem.

At another level, governments and probably private companies and trades unions (where they exist) are likely to be concerned by poverty's economic constraints on growth, investment and employment.

Activity 1

Now I want you to think about our questions: why does poverty matter and to whom?

Make brief notes in the following grid (or make your own). I've summarized my economic points as an example. There aren't any 'correct' or definitive answers but your reading of the Course Book should have given you some ideas. Don't worry if you can only think of one point for each heading.

(Spend no more than 45 minutes on this activity)

	Why poverty might matter	*To whom*
economically	Constrains growth by reducing labour productivity, investment and incomes.	Individuals, households, governments, companies and trade unions.
morally		
politically		
environmentally		
technologically		
globally		

Comment

These are some of the points that strike me but they are by no means comprehensive and may well differ from yours. (I refer several times to specific parts of the Course Book here, should you need to refer back to it.)

Morally

The idea that poverty matters morally is often related to some sense of justice or belief in human equality. We perceive people as 'poor' (in whatever sense) only because we also perceive others as 'rich'. The concept of poverty therefore inherently implies inequality which many people feel, for religious or ideological reasons, is wrong and constitutes social injustice. This judgement can, of course, be applied to inequalities between individuals, and within social institutions such as households, class and gender relations in addition to inequalities between nations. We shall return to these issues later when we look at the relationship between poverty and inequality in more detail.

But ethical concerns may not necessarily be based on an aversion to inequality. Many people simply believe that it is morally wrong for people to have to suffer the effects of poverty: for example ill-health, ignorance, malnutrition and insecurity.

Of course, moral views about issues of social justice matter to individuals. Such views underlie and reflect the fundamental ideological tensions between those who believe that economic growth is the answer to poverty and those who argue that, while growth is important, its effects are not necessarily beneficial to the poor and that they often exacerbate inequalities. This argument that development as economic growth does not necessarily lead to poverty reduction (Figure 2.1) is made at the very beginning of the first chapter in the Course Book. These different views are reflected at the macro level by governments and by institutions such as the World Bank, World Trade Organization and the United Nations Development Programme (UNDP). Nevertheless, whatever their views as to how poverty should be tackled, the subject is now firmly on the agenda of all these institutions and we shall be exploring the views of some of them in Part 2.

Figure 2.1 Poverty is a universal problem. The UK is one of the richest countries in the world, yet thousands of old people die unnecessarily during cold weather due to poor housing and low incomes.

Politically

Poverty can make people desperate and angry. They might be driven to violence either to get what material goods they need or give vent to their feelings of powerlessness. This violence may take place within households (where women are particularly vulnerable in all societies; Course Book, p.387) or in the wider community (Course Book, p.432 on poverty and urban violence). At the very least, such actions spread feelings of insecurity.

At a more organized level, poor people and their supporters might engage in political activity that destabilizes societies, making them difficult to govern and unattractive to both domestic and foreign investors, especially if the conflicts lead to civil war (Course Book, p.174). This would obviously matter to affected governments and to anyone or any company with a stake in the country. At the beginning of the twenty-first century, South Africa, for example, is experiencing increasing levels of violence as frustration mounts over the government's inability to tackle poverty and inequality – both legacies of apartheid. But we musn't assume that states are always neutral or benign victims of political unrest due to poverty. State action or inaction can itself be a major cause of poverty and inequality. You have already seen evidence of this in the UK and Brazil in the Course Book (boxes 1.5 and 1.6, pp.17–18).

Environmentally

Poverty also matters for the environment. In Chapter 7 of the Course Book, Philip Woodhouse argues that much environmental degradation in less industrialized countries is the result of poor people struggling to gain a livelihood by increasing the production of primary commodities on which they are so heavily dependent. And these local struggles for survival are linked, both historically and currently, to international factors.

Historically, colonialism fostered the production of primary commodities in the colonies (Course Book, section 11.3) and this form of production still predominates in sub-Saharan Africa whilst continuing to be vital for much of Latin America as well (Course Book, table 7.1, p.150).

Unfortunately, the prices of most primary commodities have been on a declining trend for over a century while the prices of manufactures have risen (Course Book, figure 7.4, p.151). So those countries which rely heavily on exporting primary commodities and importing manufactured goods are facing increasingly unequal international terms of trade. Yet they have no option but to go on exporting in order to earn foreign exchange, not only to buy imported goods but to pay off their debts. And since the prices of their exports tend to fall, they have to exploit their physical resources more in order to try and increase their output which, in turn, tends to depress prices even further. This is a vicious circle based on international inequalities which both exacerbate the impoverished lives of millions and contribute to the degradation of the very environment on which they have to rely for their livelihoods.

Technologically

Technology is, of course, closely related to issues of production and the environment. In general technology can enhance productivity by increasing the efficiency of the production process. But poverty can prevent the adoption of helpful technology – and not just because poor people might not be able to afford it. As Wilson and Heeks explain:

> An important dimension of being poor is that one survives in a risky environment, and certainly one's sources of livelihood are continually at risk. Thus, strategies

operated by poor people themselves are often aimed at reducing risk ... [This] means that the poor are often averse to taking part in risky ventures. Their acceptance or rejection of a new technology, therefore, is often a matter of a finely balanced calculation between the possible promises of a better livelihood by adopting it and of the risk of it failing to deliver.

Risk aversity, therefore, can be an impediment to technological development among poor people.

(Wilson and Heeks, Course Book, p.421)

The problem of risk, and helping the poor to manage it, is a major theme in the World Bank's current strategy for poverty reduction (World Bank, 2000/2001) and will be discussed further in Part 2.

The adverse effects of poverty on acquiring useful technology matter at all levels from the individual and household to the national as poor countries struggle to compete in the international economic arena.

Globally
In a world dominated by capitalism and intensified international competition, poor people are increasingly vulnerable to the effects of the globalization of capital, production and trade. This vulnerability and inability to benefit from the capitalist system translates into increasing inequalities both within and between countries with the poor becoming even more marginalized (Course Book, pp.353–354). This, in turn, takes us back to some of the moral and political implications of poverty and to related issues in one of the other course Themes, *Displacement*.

By its very nature, globalization has an international focus, but its roots and effects must also be understood at the local level, from individuals and households through to communities and countries. Poverty exists in all countries even though it may have different connotations in different places. It, therefore, matters to all countries at the very least in as much as it constrains their international competitiveness. Poverty also matters to another set of players – transnational corporations – whose aim to expand their global markets is frustrated by millions of impoverished consumers.

Now you might have noticed that in the discussion above I have often referred to poor 'people' or 'individuals' as though they were all the same. Clearly they are not. We can differentiate people objectively in terms of social class, gender, age and (crudely) rural or urban living. Poor people, like everyone else, would certainly differentiate themselves according to their own interests, values, beliefs, priorities and aspirations. All these bases of differentiation are examples of *structures* which shape the actions (*agency*) of individuals. Furthermore, many poor people complement their personal endeavours with co-operative or communal action with others, whether for economic, political or social ends. We shall pick up these ideas later when we look in more detail at what can be done about poverty (Section 7).

You may or may not agree with my views and you may have completely different answers from mine, but this exercise doesn't just help us to think about why poverty matters and to whom. It also shows that:

- poverty is multidimensional (we have touched on low incomes and growth, unemployment, poor mental and physical health, inequality, violence, degraded environments, inadequate technology and vulnerability – we shall cover more aspects as the Introduction proceeds);

- poverty doesn't only affect the poor; it also affects everyone else to some extent.

We are now going to look at some conceptual bases of poverty because we need to understand its various possible meanings if we are going to try and analyse it, measure it and evaluate proposals to tackle it.

3 Conceptions of poverty

Poverty, like many concepts, is a *contested* concept. This means that people argue over its meaning and they do so because poverty (like, for example, development, democracy or social justice) is not a natural or unchanging fact. It is a social construct. That is to say, its definitions are socially determined and subject to debate and change as social conditions and values alter. This is well explained in the quotation from Bauman in the Course Book pp.14–15, so you might like to remind yourself of it now.

This social basis of poverty means that its definitions may differ both between societies and within them. So what richer people might regard as poverty may not be so regarded by someone from a poorer society or a poorer section of their own society. This reflects the idea of *relative* poverty (Course Book, pp.12–13).

Activity 2

Let's start by refreshing our memories. Have a quick skim through Section 1.2 of Chapter 1 in the Course Book and note the different definitions of poverty.

(Spend only 10 minutes on this)

Comment

I hope you've written down something similar to the following:

poverty as

- low income
- social exclusion
- multiple deprivations
- failure of capabilities
- linked to social disintegration and environmental destruction as part of a global crisis.

Of course these conceptions of poverty are not mutually exclusive and it is perfectly possible, in principle, to use them all in trying to get to grips with the nature and extent of poverty. What particular conceptions are chosen will depend on factors such as your standpoint, your aims and the availability of data.

Here I want us to explore a little more the conceptions of poverty as multiple deprivations, failure of capabilities and social exclusion. (I'm not ignoring the other conceptions. Low income is often part of exclusion, deprivation and capability failure and we shall discuss it in those contexts. Poverty as part of the global crisis seems to me to be not a different conception of poverty but rather another level at which to analyse it; we shall take it up in Section 4.)

3.1 Poverty as multiple deprivations

In the Course Book several chapters are devoted to various different aspects of the poverty hydra. They cover famine, hunger, disease, high mortality rates, unemployment, low income, high fertility rates, environmental degradation and war. All these aspects of poverty also have a gender dimension, i.e. they tend to affect men and women differently.

However, poverty is not simply a collection of separate deprivations. It is a complexity in which various deprivations often reinforce each other. This might appear to make the problem completely intractable but the very interrelationship of poverty's facets means that tackling one can often indirectly ameliorate others. As the World Bank Report *Attacking Poverty* says:

> Improving health outcomes not only improves well-being but also increases income-earning potential. Increasing education not only improves well-being – it also leads to better health outcomes and to higher incomes. Providing protection for poor people (reducing vulnerability in dealing with risk) not only makes them feel less vulnerable – it also allows them to take advantage of higher-risk, higher-return opportunities. Increasing poor people's voice and participation not only addresses their sense of exclusion – it also leads to better targeting of health and education services to their needs. Understanding these complementarities is essential for designing and implementing programs and projects that help people escape poverty.
>
> (World Bank, 2000/2001, pp.15–16)

This passage does slightly give the impression that, once the complexities of poverty have been grasped, the solution is essentially a technical one of providing health, jobs, education, protection and participation. At this stage we just need to note that such provisions are not simply a matter of money, skills and technology even if these are available. Tackling poverty is also, fundamentally, a *political* matter involving conflict over interests, values and resources within households, communities and states and at the international level (Figure 3.1). We shall return to these issues in Section 7 below.

You will have noticed, in the passage quoted above, the concept of *vulnerability* which was used for the first time by the World Bank in 2000 as an indicator of poverty. Vulnerability is exposure to risk from a number of possible sources such as loss of job, land or income, and natural disasters, illness, domestic violence, crime, war, global climate change and so on. These sort of factors are the immediate cause of vulnerability but

> ...the deeper cause is the inability to reduce or mitigate risk or cope with shocks – a cause that both draws from and feeds into the causes of other dimensions of poverty. Low levels of physical, natural, and financial assets make poor people especially vulnerable to negative shocks – those

Figure 3.1 Poverty is a political matter: protestors outside the World Trade Organization meeting in Seattle, 1999. The WTO believes that free trade benefits poor countries but its critics argue that free trade mainly benefits rich countries and transnational corporations.

with more assets can weather these shocks as long as they are temporary. Lack of adequate assets can set up a vicious downward spiral in which actions to cope in the short term worsen deprivation in the long term. Pulling children out of school to earn extra income during an economic crisis. Depleting natural resources beyond the sustainable level. Making quick sales of land or livestock at desperately low prices. Lowering nutritional intake below the levels necessary to sustain health.

Another underlying cause of vulnerability is the inability of the state or community to develop mechanisms to reduce or mitigate the risks that poor people face.

(World Bank, 2000/2001, pp.36–37)

The concept of vulnerability, then, helps to direct attention not only to the multiple and interrelated causes of poverty but to its dynamic nature – sometimes attempts by individuals and households to ameliorate one aspect immediately can worsen others eventually. Poverty as vulnerability will be explored further in Part 2.

3.2 Poverty as failure of capabilities

This conception builds on the idea of poverty as multiple deprivations and not simply as a function of low income.

As Alan Thomas writes in the Course Book, p.14:

...Sen puts forward a view of poverty which derives from the idea of failure to be able to take a full part in human society but which sees this as a matter of lack of choice or capability rather than simply material living standards.

As an economist, Sen felt that the emphasis of classical economics on economic growth and individuals' material well-being was too narrow and ignored many other valued aspects of people's lives such as political participation, physical and mental health, education, cultural pursuits and so on. This view reflects very closely the idea of development as 'the realization of human potential' (Course Book, pp.32–34). Income matters, but only as a means to the end of improving opportunities and capabilities. Nevertheless, the effect of income on capabilities will depend on what Sen calls 'contingent circumstances, both personal and social' (Sen, 1999, p.70). He makes four points in this respect:

■ The relationship between income and capabilities is strongly affected by social factors such as age, gender, health and social responsibilities; and by people's environment which may be prone to floods or drought or engender insecurity due to violence.

■ Some groups such as old, ill and disabled people are in a double bind because they probably need more income to meet their needs yet the ability to earn that income is reduced by their condition.

■ Figures on family or household income tell us nothing about the distribution of that income within the family or household. He points out that in much of Asia and North Africa there is likely to be a gender bias in favour of males.

■ Relative income deprivation is an important consideration and locates poverty in its social context. So being relatively income-poor in a rich country can lead to social exclusion because the impoverished cannot afford the things deemed necessary to participate in society even though in poorer societies such levels of deprivation might be regarded as wealth.

(Sen, 1999, pp.88–89)

The link between personal incomes and capabilities is, therefore, by no means straightforward.

Sen argues that capabilities to some extent depend on people's *entitlements* and that these are, in turn, affected by people's *endowments*. You came across these concepts in the Course Book in relation to Sen's analysis of the causes of famine. Go back now to the Course Book, p.60, and remind yourself of their meanings. It is important to appreciate that endowments are strongly affected in all societies by structural factors such as gender, class, age and perhaps ethnicity.

But capabilities don't just depend on people's private endowments and entitlements. They can also be considerably enhanced by public provisioning of services such as health, education, transport and sanitation. For example, Parker and Wilson (Course Book, section 4.4) draw on Sen's work in relation to health to show how a poor country like Sri Lanka has a much lower under-five mortality rate than many other countries with a similar or higher GNP per capita. By contrast, Brazil, with a GNP per capita six times bigger than Sri Lanka's, has about twice its under-five mortality rate. The reasons for Sri Lanka's good record on this and other poverty indicators are complex but one of the most important factors has been the much better public provisioning and long history of public participation in Sri Lanka. These reflect the importance of public action in tackling poverty. The concept of public action is discussed in detail in *Study Guide 1*, Section 10. We shall refer to public action several times in this Introduction, so it may be a good time to remind yourself of its meaning now.

Sen's work has a strong emphasis on individuals and agency. This is not very surprising given that he defines development as the enhancement of *individuals'* capabilities. Nevertheless, he also recognizes the importance of structure:

> …individual agency is, ultimately, central to addressing these deprivations. On the other hand, the freedom of agency that we individually have is inescapably qualified and constrained by the social, political and economic opportunities that are available to us. There is a deep complementarity between individual agency and social arrangements.
>
> (Sen, 1999, pp.xi–xii)

The 'social, political and economic opportunities' in the passage above refer to the freedoms we may or may not have in these spheres to realize our capabilities. Sen sees *freedom* not only as the primary *goal* of development but also as a *means* to it. Therefore, political, social and economic freedoms are not only desirable in their own right, but as the means for people to achieve their capabilities (or avoid deprivation). However, freedoms are embedded in and protected by social institutions or 'social arrangements' such as the state, political parties, legal and financial systems, markets, trade unions, public interest NGOs and so on. Sen argues that individual freedom is, therefore, a social product because there is a two-way relationship between (a) social arrangements to expand individual freedoms and (b) the use of individual freedoms not only to improve individuals' own lives but to engage in public action to make social institutions more appropriate and effective in facilitating everyone's capabilities. So public participation is vital both in determining the values and institutions in society which affect freedoms, and capabilities and in ensuring that these institutions facilitate them.

Figure 3.2 attempts to summarize the main elements affecting people's capabilities, but do remember that the effects of income, endowments and entitlements are, in turn, mediated by factors such as age, gender, health, social responsibilities and so on.

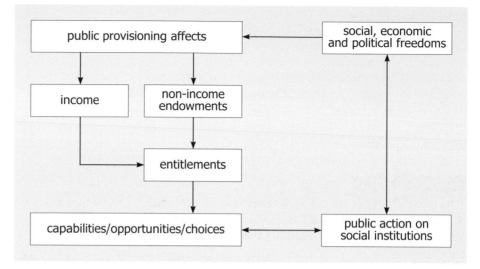

Figure 3.2 Factors influencing capabilities.

Sen's view of poverty, then, has the merits of being broad and of directing our attention to the political, economic and social structures that cause or maintain poverty. But is it too broad to be able to distinguish serious poverty from mere frustration at marginal limitations to our lives and capabilities? We shall discuss this further in Section 5.

3.3 Poverty as social exclusion

In the Course Book, p.14, Alan Thomas quotes the European Foundation's definition of social exclusion:

> …the process through which individuals or groups are wholly or partially excluded from full participation in the society in which they live.

This is closely related to Sen's view of poverty as the inability to lead the kind of life one values. People may be excluded because they lack endowments or because they can't translate their endowments into entitlements due to processes and institutions that exclude them from participation.

Turn to the Course Book p.121 and have a careful look at Table 5.6 'Arenas and elements of social exclusion'. You will see that social exclusion has been broken down into three key 'arenas' – rights, resources and relationships. Another way of looking at these arenas is to see them as political (rights), economic (resources) and social (relationships). It doesn't matter which set of concepts you use; the important thing to note is that social exclusion can cover all aspects of life. Nevertheless, this doesn't mean that someone has to be excluded in all areas to feel impoverished. They may, for example, have full political rights but inadequate income or poor education.

Look at the right-hand column in Table 5.6 of the Course Book where each arena is broken down further into 'elements'.

Now, make a list of the elements and next to each one write some very brief notes about what you think each one means or give some examples to illustrate what it means. You will find most of the elements in the Course Book so a good place to start is the index.

(Spend no more than 20 minutes on this activity)

Comment

You can check your answers against mine in Appendix 1. I didn't have much trouble with the elements under 'resources' and 'relationships' although I think the line between 'wider support networks' and 'voluntary organizations' seems a bit blurred.

I also noted that 'state provision' isn't fixed and unchanging. What states provide and to whom arises from the particular conditions of any society, depending on its history, its resources and, crucially, on what politicians and the public think *should* be provided by the state. But there might be considerable disagreement about all this (those of you familiar with public debate in Britain over the last twenty years will be aware of conflicting views over what the state should provide in areas of, for example, health, public transport and social security). What the state provides, and arguments about what it should provide, are part of the idea of public action.

I found the elements listed under 'rights' posed quite a problem of definition because, of all the elements listed, human, legal and democratic rights are the most contested. They are not the same in all countries, which isn't surprising as they arise from historical struggles within societies (e.g. the French Revolution) or between societies (e.g. colonial independence movements). Even today some countries such as China regard attempts to get them to agree to the Universal Declaration of Human Rights as, at best, an infringement of sovereignty and, at worst, an example of Western imperialism.

I asked you simply to make notes on each element of social exclusion but you may well have noticed possible connections between the separate elements. For example, exclusion from rights of citizenship or exclusion from education are likely to mean exclusion from formal employment opportunities.

The UNDP's Human Development Report *Human Rights and Human Development* (UNDP, 2000) lists the following fundamental human rights (p.1):

- freedom from discrimination – by gender, race, ethnicity, national origin or religion;
- freedom from want – to enjoy a decent standard of living;
- freedom to develop and realize one's human potential;
- freedom from fear of threats to personal security, from torture, arbitrary arrest and other violent acts;
- freedom from injustice and violations of the rule of law;

- freedom of thought and speech and to participate in decision-making and form associations;
- freedom for decent work – without exploitation.

This linking of rights and freedoms to inclusion and participation reflects the importance that, as we saw, Sen attaches to freedom and capabilities. But how does the social exclusion approach help us to understand poverty?

First of all, it enables us to see that poverty may have many causes (political, economic and social) and that these often interact to reinforce each other.

Second, it enables us to think about the sort of questions we need to ask if we are to understand *why* people become impoverished and excluded.

However, we need to be aware of some possible problems associated with the idea of social exclusion:

1   We can't assume that someone who appears to be excluded feels impoverished or unhappy about it. They may have *chosen* not to participate or be included in the mainstream.

2   Whilst we are concerned here with exclusion as poverty, we must not forget that the rich often exclude themselves from mainstream society by, for example, buying private health and education services. This may make them less likely to push for the provision of good public services for everyone else, especially the poor. (But recall the example of the growth of public sanitation in *Study Guide 1*, Section 10. At first the rich made private arrangements for themselves but then lobbied for public provision when they realized that if the rich were to avoid disease, the poor also needed sanitation.)

3   Attitudes to social exclusion are often bound up with moral views about its causes. Thus, the excluded are regarded by some as deserving of their position due to their attitudes, culture or whatever.

4   We might be tempted to assume that support for social inclusion reflects a desire for a *fairer* society, but this isn't necessarily the case. For example, governments may be keen to tackle social exclusion and cut public expenditure by getting people off unemployment benefit and into work. But the conditions of employment (e.g. low pay, insecurity, unsocial hours) for many people, and especially women, may foster and maintain inequalities.

We are now going to look at an important conception of poverty which is not discussed in the Course Book but which helps us to improve our understanding of poverty as a structural problem.

3.4 Relational and residual poverty

The *relational* view of poverty focuses on social relationships as the underlying causes of poverty:

> ...relational approaches investigate the causes of...poverty in terms of *social relations* of production and reproduction, of property and power that characterize certain kinds of development, and especially those associated with the spread and growth of capitalism. A relational approach thus asks, are some poor *because* others are rich (and vice versa)? What are the mechanisms that generate both wealth and poverty as two sides of the same coin of (capitalist) development?
>
> (Bernstein, 1992, p.24)

Conceiving poverty as relational takes us beyond the material aspects of life such as people's income or access to land or their education levels and state of health, important though these undoubtedly are. A relational approach is essentially a structuralist approach and so requires us to see how people's poverty is embedded in and nurtured by the unequal social relations in which they are caught. For example, people's income, access to land, education levels and state of health tend to be affected by their social position in relation to others within various social structures; that is, whether they are men or women (gender relations), employers or employees (relations of production), landlords or tenants (relations of property), buyers or sellers (market relations). Social relations are, not surprisingly, often characterized by conflicting values and interests.

The relational approach enhances our understanding of the causes of capability failure and social exclusion because it exposes the structural underpinnings of poverty. For example, Sen's endowments and entitlements, which so strongly affect capabilities, are, in turn, largely dependent on people's structural positions. These positions can also help explain why some people or groups find it difficult to participate and feel excluded.

In contrast to seeing poverty as relational, it may be seen as *residual*. In this conception, poverty is the result of a failure of income to trickle down to the poor. It is based on the neoliberal assumption that economic growth will benefit everyone and if it doesn't, then the answer is to give them access to resources to enable them to participate in productive activities which should solve their (income) poverty. The problem with the residual approach is that it ignores the structural causes of poverty, so attempts to tackle the effects (e.g. low income) can easily be undermined by structural constraints and inequalities.

In the Course Book (p.390), Ruth Pearson provides an implicit example of the residual approach. This was the Women in Development (WID) idea that women are excluded from development due to their lack of resources and that once they have resources they will no longer be subordinate. This view was criticized by the Gender and Development

(GAD) relational view that women's subordination is an intrinsic part of gender relations; it is these unequal relations that need tackling because it is they that fundamentally constrain women's development.

3.5 Main strengths and weaknesses of different conceptions

Tables 3.1 and 3.2 attempt to show what I think are broadly the main strengths and weaknesses of the different conceptions of poverty as a quick comparison which you may find helpful. You may disagree or want to add others – feel free!

Table 3.1 Main strengths of different conceptions of poverty

	Relatively simple to measure	Points to complexity of poverty	Focuses on mechanisms of impoverishment	Importance of structural causes	Explicit focus on lack of freedom and rights
Low income	✓		?	?	
Multiple deprivations		✓			
Capability failure		✓	✓	✓	✓
Social exclusion		✓	✓	✓	✓
Relational		✓	✓	✓	
Residual	✓				

Table 3.2 Main weaknesses of different conceptions of poverty

	Too narrow	Too broad	Difficult to measure	No focus on structural causes
Low income	✓			?
Multiple deprivations			✓	?
Capability failure		?	✓	
Social exclusion		?	✓	
Relational			✓	
Residual	✓			✓

Summary of Section 3

Now let's recap on this section:

- Poverty is socially constructed. This means that:

  it may be defined differently in different societies;

  definitions may change over time;

  within the same society different people and groups will have different views of what constitutes poverty for them and others.

- There are many ways of conceptualizing poverty:

  from the simplicity of low income to the complexity of multiple deprivations;

  as a limit on human potential and freedom;

  as a process of social exclusion;

  as a result of structural inequalities;

  as being left out of capitalist development.

- These conceptions are not mutually exclusive; in fact, they often overlap.

- We can use any or all of these conceptions to try and analyse:

  the causes of poverty;

  the links between different aspects of poverty;

  the effects of poverty.

4 Analysing poverty

We are now going to apply some of the conceptualizations of poverty from Section 3. This will be a test of their usefulness because they are only as good as their ability to help us analyse real situations of poverty.

4.1 Applying concepts of poverty

Activity 4

Read the following extract and then answer the questions below. The extract is taken from a World Bank study of the views of 60 000 poor men and women in 60 countries.

(Spend no more than 30 minutes on this activity)

The story of Murari

Murari is a 30-year old man who is presently living in the village of Kedarkui [India] with his family. He began his period of contractual labour in agriculture five years ago for a dominant Thakur caste farmer. The Thakur also acts as a moneylender in many of the surrounding villages. Five years ago Murari took out a loan of approximately Rs.1,000 that he needed for an unexpected emergency. As a term of the loan, Murari was compelled to work for the Thakur farmer as an agricultural labourer on the moneylender's land for a wage of only Rs.5,000 a year. This Thakur farmer/moneylender provided Murari and his family with accommodations, food, and some money for miscellaneous expenses, while keeping account of everything that was provided.

At the end of the first two years, Murari owed Rs.2,500 to the Thakur. After two years of labour he owed 250 percent more to the Thakur than he had initially borrowed due to the interest incurred on the loan, charges for food and accommodation, small loans provided on an ongoing basis, and so on. However, despite this dismal situation Murari was not able to leave the Thakur's farm in search of more profitable work. If he attempted to leave, ... the moneylender would track him down and the consequences would undoubtedly be serious. After five years of work as an agricultural labourer and house servant for the Thakur, Murari owes over Rs.8000. Murari and others like him find that they are virtually powerless once they enter the vicious circle of contractual labour, where they are compelled to concede to the tyranny and exploitation of the moneylenders. But for many of the poorest villagers, there are no alternative sources of loans and ... they have no choice but to accept the exploitative terms of the local moneylenders.

(Narayan *et al.*, 2000, p.63)

(a) Which elements of social exclusion listed in Table 5.6 of the Course Book can you find in the extract?

(b) How would you link the elements of social exclusion to explain Murari's position?

(c) Are there any important aspects of the situation that don't seem to be covered by the elements of social exclusion?

(d) If you were to apply a relational analysis to Murari's situation, what social relations would you say were most important in causing and maintaining his poverty?

Comment

(a) The elements of social exclusion touched on seem to me to be:

Rights

Using the list of human rights above, we see that Murari lacks several:

- freedom from want: he is heavily in debt to the farmer/moneylender despite five years' work;
- freedom to develop his own potential: he can't possibly do this while he is bound in debt to the farmer;
- freedom from fear: it is implied that he would suffer violence if he tried to escape;
- freedom from injustice and law violation: the article doesn't say so, but debt bondage is illegal in India;
- freedom to work without exploitation: the extract is explicitly about Murari's exploitation in terms of both his labour and his money.

Resources

The key elements here seem to be:

- Lack of access to the free labour market since Murari is a bonded labourer.
- Lack of access to official forms of credit (a 'product market') which is a direct result of his income poverty. Banks don't like lending to those on low income or without some form of collateral (such as land) to offset the risk of the loan.
- We can assume that Murari does not have access to any state credit schemes, if they exist in his area.

Relationships

Presumably it was Murari's inability to call on other family or wider support networks in the first place that forced him to borrow from the farmer.

(b) By linking the elements above, we can see how social exclusion is both a cause and effect of poverty, i.e. we can start to understand it as a *process*:

The *causal* chain began (at least, in the extract) with the emergency for which Murari needed money and which exposed his vulnerability to forces outside his control. Excluded from official credit sources and wider support networks, he was forced to work for the man who lent him the money.

The interrelated *effects* were Murari's debt bondage, a form of labour introduced during the colonial period (Course Book, p.259) which excluded him from more profitable work, largely because he feared violence from the farmer if he tried to get away. And, finally, he became more indebted than ever, thus tying him even more firmly to the moneylender and increasing his poverty.

(c) There seems to be one particularly important aspect of Murari's situation which is not covered by the elements of social exclusion. This is the *inequality* in the relationship between Murari and the Thakur. Murari and his family are entirely dependent on the farmer for accommodation, food and money and Murari is completely exploited. Moreover, his labour is exacerbating the inequality by contributing to the wealth of the farmer. This inequality, cemented by the threat of violence and the inefficacy of the law, makes Murari, as the extract says, 'virtually powerless'.

(d) The crucial social relations which appear to have caused and maintained Murari's impoverished situation are those of:

- caste: caste is an intrinsically unequal social structure; we are told that the farmer is of the dominant Thakur caste so we can assume that Murari is of a lesser caste;

- landlord and tenant;

- creditor and debtor;

- employer and labourer.

We have only applied the concepts of social exclusion and relational poverty to our analysis of Murari's story as I thought they would probably be the most fruitful. We were able to apply these concepts because the story provided answers to the sorts of questions these conceptions ask about structural relations and access to resources. I hope you will agree that, in combination, they have been useful, not only in understanding the structural processes and institutions behind his poverty but in showing the links between different aspects of his poverty and even hinting at the nature of his capability deprivation (although we couldn't be sure of that without asking Murari what he would like to be and do).

Activity 5

Read the extracts 'Poverty in the UK' and 'Poverty in a Brazilian city' in the Course Book pp.17–18 and then answer the following questions. You can check your answers with mine in Appendix 1.

(Don't spend more than 45 minutes on this activity)

(a) For each case study, make a list of all the elements of poverty, both material and non-material.

(b) Would you say the elements of poverty were quite similar or very different in the two studies?

(c) From the UK example, write down
- what likely *causes* of unemployment you can identify from your list;
- what likely *effects* of unemployment you can identify from your list.

(d) Would you be able to decide, from the evidence in these two extracts, how the people's capabilities were affected by poverty? Explain your answer.

This exercise should have brought home to you the reinforcing multidimensionality and complexity of poverty even though the two extracts ignore a lot of important questions, such as the causes of high unemployment and benefit cuts in the UK and the causes of the great migration to the Amazon in Brazil. Nor are we told, for example, how poverty impacts differently on men and women or different ethnic groups.

Again, I directed you to use certain conceptualizations of poverty (multiple deprivations and failure of capabilities) in your analysis but these are not the only possibilities. A social exclusion approach would also have yielded useful insights.

4.2 Analysing the causes and effects of poverty at the international level

Having applied concepts of poverty to households and communities, let's now see how useful they are for understanding the creation and reinforcement of poverty at the international level.

Korten's view of poverty as part of a 'global crisis' (Course Book, p.19) points to the necessity of widening our lens to view poverty in an international context. But to what extent will the conceptualizations from Section 3 be useful in our analysis?

Focusing on international aspects of poverty entails examining structural relationships between countries which seem to play a part in exacerbating or ameliorating poverty. This implies that it might be useful to start with a *relational* approach in order to examine the role of market relations (e.g. trade and investment) and institutional structures (e.g. the IMF, World Bank and TNCs) in linking rich and poor countries.

If we look at the broad economic changes that occurred in the world in the last half of the twentieth century (Course Book, ch.13) it is striking that the decisions which led to those changes were, to a large extent, in the hands of states and institutions in the developed countries (italicized in the discussion below). The only major intentional and independent economic action by developing countries that had an international impact was the raising of the oil price by OPEC* first in 1973 and again in 1979. The following points illustrate the powerful role played by dominant structures and agents in influencing the fate of poor countries.

*Oil Producing and Exporting Countries.

- The *World Bank and the IMF* (both dominated by governments of rich countries) set the international economic scenery in place after the Second World War and still have a very powerful influence today as money-lenders, giving them heavy leverage over poor countries' economies and polities via structural adjustment programmes, 'good governance' agreements and poverty reduction strategies in return for promised debt reduction. At a meeting of the G8* leading industrial countries in Cologne in 1999, it was agreed that US$100bn of debt relief would be available for the most highly indebted countries and that the process would begin by the end of 2000. So far the process has been very slow, partly due to the refusal of the *US Congress* to vote the necessary funds. Critics argue that the amount of debt relief is too small anyway and meanwhile many countries have debts far higher than their GNPs and spend more on debt repayments than on health and education.*

*USA, Germany, UK, Canada, France, Italy, Japan and Russian Federation.

*Debt is discussed on the audio programme 'Does Dropping the Debt Miss the Point?'. You might like to listen to it now if you haven't done so already.

- *European commercial banks* were responsible for lending the recycled oil money (after the 1973 oil price rise by OPEC) to poor countries at low interest rates with little concern about the viability of the loans or the possibility that interest rates might rise to damaging levels for poor countries.

- *OECD governments* put up interest rates and trade barriers in the 1970s and 1980s in order to counter recession. This led to increased debt repayments for poor countries and a shrinking market for their exports (the main source of the foreign exchange needed to repay debts). There has also been a steady decline in official aid since the mid 1980s.

- Recession also led to declining demand for primary commodities by *manufacturing companies* in industrialized countries and this, in turn, led to a huge fall in prices in *western commodity markets* in the 1980s, a trend which has since continued. And since primary commodities constitute a large percentage of the export earnings of the most heavily indebted regions (Latin America and sub-Saharan Africa), a fall in their value is very bad news both for their balance of payments and for the incomes of their producers, vast numbers of whom are small-scale peasant farmers.

- *Transnational corporations* were important direct investors in some developing countries in the 1960s but their relative influence declined over the next couple of decades as southern governments preferred to borrow money and invest it as they saw fit. The situation changed during the 1990s with economic liberalization (often under the duress of structural adjustment) and the recognition that foreign direct investment (FDI) can bring in not only capital but also expertise, technology and links to international markets (World Bank, 1999/2000,

Figure 4.1 The ubiquitous McDonald's logo – a powerful symbol of foreign direct investment here in Beijing, 2000.

pp.36–37; Figure 4.1). By 1997 about half of all capital flows to developing countries were from TNCs but the distribution between those countries was very uneven, so some benefited far more than others, as Table 4.1 shows.

Table 4.1 Distribution of FDI in developing countries as a percentage of total world FDI, 1997

Argentina, Brazil and Mexico	7.2
Other Latin America	3.7
China (inc. Hong Kong)	7.1
South-east Asia	7.3
Other Asia	2.8
Sub-Saharan Africa	1.9
Others	0.3
Total	30.3

Source: World Bank (1999/2000) *World Development Report*, Oxford University Press, New York, p.38.

There is much debate over the impact of TNCs on poverty and each case has to be judged on its merits. They may well foster employment and growth and introduce new technology and markets. On the other hand, they may foster enclave development with few linkages to the rest of the economy and few skilled or managerial employment opportunities for local people. They are sometimes accused of cultural imperialism (Coca-Cola and McDonald's come instantly to mind) and they are in business to make profits, a high proportion of which may be repatriated and so not available to the host country.

■ *Foreign portfolio investors* (i.e. foreigners buying shares in companies in developing countries) are also sources of capital which can boost investment but such capital can also be taken out of countries very quickly, making them very vulnerable. A central feature of the East Asian crisis of 1997/8 was massive new inflows of short-term capital in the early 1990s followed by a sudden reversal in 1997. Net financial inflows to Indonesia, South Korea, Malaysia, Philippines and Thailand totalled $97bn in 1996; in just a few weeks in 1997 they had a total net outflow of $12bn – a loss of $109bn (i.e. they lost the $97bn plus $12bn more) equal to more than 10% of their combined GDPs (Shirazi, 1998). Controlling these capital flows is very difficult. The economist James Tobin has suggested a tax on all international currency transactions to try and deter speculators or at least make them pay for their gains. Such a tax seems unlikely in the current climate of liberalization.

■ *Information technology* has been developed in the rich countries and is controlled by companies in those countries, but its use is increasingly vital for the competitive production and distribution of goods and services. Table 4.2 illustrates just how big the gap is between the rich and poor countries of the world in terms of Internet access.

Table 4.2 Internet access

Users	Population as % of world population	Internet access as % of regional population
USA	4.7	26.3
OECD (excl. USA)	14.1	6.9
Latin America and Caribbean	6.8	0.8
South-east Asia and Pacific	8.6	0.5
East Asia	22.2	0.4
East Europe and CIS	5.8	0.4
Arab States	4.5	0.2
Sub-Saharan Africa	9.7	0.1
South Asia	23.5	0.04

Source: UNDP (1999) *Human Development Report*, Oxford University Press, p.63.

■ *Restructuring of capitalism.* Harriss uses this phrase (Course Book, ch.15) to capture the many economic changes (with political and social ramifications) that were sparked by the recession from 1973, although the roots of such changes were implanted before that. These economic changes resulted in a shift towards flexible production processes, facilitated by information technology and the liberalization of markets for goods, capital and labour as part of the prevailing ideology of neoliberalism.

What effect has all this had on poverty? Flexible production processes and liberalization have meant that companies can invest more easily where they think they will get the best returns. Some developing countries have benefited from this but the effect has been very uneven as we saw in Table 4.1 above. And we can't assume that FDI will benefit poor people within any particular country.

One of the major effects of flexibility has been on the labour force as jobs become more insecure. The increase in part-time and temporary jobs as well as the increasing propensity for people to work at home all reduce the ability of labour to organize collectively. This makes all workers, but particularly the less skilled, more vulnerable to fluctuations in markets and to management decisions to sack workers, relocate production or reduce wages.

The ascendancy of neoliberal ideas from the 1980s also resulted in restructuring the role of states, traditional 'protectors' of the poor against the harsh effects of markets. In all developing countries forced to implement structural adjustment policies, there have been cuts in public expenditure in vital areas such as health and education. Table 4.3 gives some examples of the consequences of these cuts for Africa in general and some particular African countries.

Table 4.3 Changes in some social indicators during structural adjustment

	Enrolment ratios[a] 1980	Enrolment ratios 1990	Persons per doctor 1984	Persons per doctor 1990	Persons per nurse 1984	Persons per nurse 1990
Africa	39	35	24 600	35 680	2200	8190
Ghana	48	46	14 900	25 000	600	2750
Ivory Coast	39	37	NA	16670	NA	3470
Kenya	62	58	10 100	71 430	1000	22 320
Madagascar	60	40	10 000	8330	NA	2380
Nigeria	50	37	8000	66 670	1000	11 110
Tanzania	44	32	NA	33 330	NA	4570

[a]Enrolment ratios measure the number of students enrolled in a level of education as a percentage of the population aged 6–23.

NA = not available

Source: Lensink, R. (1996) *Structural Adjustment in Sub-Saharan Africa*, Longman Publishing, London, table 8.2, p.117.

Although we can identify the main institutions and processes that seem to have had such an international impact in the last fifty years, there is considerable disagreement over what effect they have all had on poverty. For example, in relation to Table 4.3, although the changes occurred during a period of structural adjustment, it is difficult to prove that they were entirely due to those policies.

The *relational* conception of poverty has, I think, been very useful in directing our attention to some important international links and inequalities which might help explain why some countries remain poor at a time of international economic growth. However, our analysis might be enriched by using other conceptualizations as well. For example, we might use Sen's concepts of *endowments and entitlements* to investigate in more depth the issues of production in poor countries and international trade. Such an approach would prompt us to ask questions such as:

■ To what extent is production in poor countries constrained by their natural endowments?

- Who owns or controls their productive assets and to whose benefit?
- What are the problems in trying to increase and diversify their exports?
- Can commodity markets be regulated to favour poor producers?
- Does free trade harm or help poor countries' imports and exports?
- To what extent are global processes undermining national and local social provisioning of services and reducing poor people's access to them?

Alternatively or additionally, it might be helpful to think of international poverty in terms of *social exclusion* at the global level. So, for example, we might want to know more about *why* some countries attract so little foreign investment (Table 4.1 above) or the *effects* of lack of access to information technology (Table 4.2 above) on countries' ability to participate fruitfully in the international economy.

Summary of Section 4

In this section, we have applied various conceptions of poverty at the individual, national and international levels. As a teacher, I chose the conceptions for each analysis on the basis of what I thought would be most fruitful for showing you how they could be applied, but as a policy-maker, I might have chosen different ones or different combinations.

As we saw in Section 3, no conception of poverty is perfect, so it isn't surprising that we may find some more useful and attractive than others depending on our own views of poverty and its causes. However, the conceptions we use also depend partly on the type of information available and what we want to use it for. These issues are taken up again in the next section.

5 Measuring poverty

5.1 The importance of statistics

In the last section we analysed several cases of poverty (Murari's story and urban poverty in the UK and Brazil) without using any measurements. In other words, we used a *qualitative* approach to explore processes, institutions and, crucially, relationships which seemed to foster poverty and inequality. But measurement, or a *quantitative* approach, is also an important part of poverty analysis, as we saw in Section 4.2. This is because measurement can provide us with evidence which may throw light on the magnitude, causes and effects of poverty and on how poverty changes over time. Measurement can also provide evidence on the impact of poverty-reduction policies. The ability to collect and analyse data on a large scale is, therefore, a particularly important basis for policy-making and evaluation:

> Better, more reliable statistics are an essential element in improving the ability of national governments to formulate appropriate policies, manage their own economic and social development, and monitor improvements in their living standards. Too often, out-dated, missing or unreliable information leads to badly informed decisions, which waste resources and incur high financial and human costs. For example, two-fifths of the world's children live in countries where it is not known how many children are in primary school.
>
> (World Bank, 1999)

"That's the gist of what I want to say. Now get me some statistics to base it on."

Figure 5.1

Quantitative evidence *per se* is not necessarily more reliable than qualitative but it does allow us to complement qualitative information which is often obtained at the level of the individual, household or small community.

5.2 Some problems of poverty measurement

The passage from the World Bank quoted above points to some of the problems of poverty measurement, relating to the collection and reliability of statistics, but there are other problems. These relate to the conceptualization of poverty and I want to draw your attention to two important aspects here.

1   The first concerns the problem of trying to capture the *complexity* of poverty in statistical form.

Much of the poverty data presented in the Course Book is either based on a single indicator such as GNP per capita, infant mortality, adult literacy, and employment or else on the composite Human Development Index (HDI).[*]

[*]HDI is explained in the Course Book, p.16.

The problem with using single indicators is that they are just that, and so give only a limited view of poverty. On the other hand, they can be very useful precisely because they *do* throw light on specific problems. If, for example, you want to know about life expectancy, it is better to use that than the HDI which includes life expectancy as only one of its components.

The HDI is an attempt to combine economic and social factors in a more general welfare measure. To that extent, it is an improvement on using a single indicator but it still has two problems. First, like all the other indicators, it is an average and so tells us nothing about the distribution of well-being within a country. Second, its components are equally and arbitrarily weighted as if they are equally important aspects of poverty or development.

2   The second problem of poverty measurement relates to different *conceptions* of poverty. Different indicators reflect different conceptual assumptions about the nature of poverty and both of these affect the sort of policy solutions put forward, as the following activity demonstrates.

Activity 6

Look at Tables 5.1 and 5.2 below and then answer the following questions:

(a) If you were to judge development in terms of income alone, which country would you say was most developed and which least developed?

(b) If you were to judge development in terms of the broader indicator of HDI, which country would you say was most developed and which least developed?

(c) Do the data support the idea that the best way to ameliorate poverty is to increase incomes?

(d) Drawing on other parts of the course, how might you explain the fact that China and Sri Lanka have similar HDIs to much richer countries?

Note that GDP is measured at PPP or 'purchasing power parity'. Check the definition in the Course Book, Box 1.3, p.12.

(Spend 15 minutes on this activity. The answers are in Appendix 1.)

Table 5.1 Similar incomes with different HDI

	GDP per capita (US$ PPP 1998)	HDI value 1998
Chile	8787	0.826
Malaysia	8137	0.772
South Africa	8488	0.697

Source: UNDP (2000) *Human Development Report*, Oxford University Press, New York, pp.157–159.

Table 5.2 Similar HDI with different incomes

	HDI value 1998	GDP per capita (US$ PPP 1998)
Saudi Arabia	0.747	10 158
Brazil	0.747	6625
Philippines	0.744	3555
Sri Lanka	0.733	2979
China	0.706	3105

Source: UNDP (2000) *Human Development Report*, Oxford University Press, New York, pp.157–159.

The last activity demonstrates the care required to interpret data. It isn't simply a matter of examining the figures but of asking exactly what they are measuring. It is important for you to bear this in mind when interpreting statistical data. For example:

■ Those who take a *residual approach* see poverty as essentially an economic issue and will tend to use mainly economic indicators such as income measures. Their solutions are likely to be based on attempts to improve the earning capacity of the poor. This, for a long time, was the World Bank's position.

■ By contrast, those such as Sen who see poverty as *capability failure* are more likely to use single social indicators such as health and education or the composite HDI and HPI* (Box 5.1). Solutions would centre round trying to improve people's health, education, income and so on in order to facilitate their participation in society and improve their choices. In Section 3.2 above, I raised the question of

*HPI (Human Poverty Index) is explained in the Course Book, p.16.

whether Sen's conception of poverty was too broad to be useful in distinguishing different degrees of poverty. If we were to try and compare individuals we would have to evaluate their capabilities, but how would we measure them and what relative importance would we attach to different capabilities? How would we get a picture of poverty in a whole community or society by using the capabilities approach? These questions indicate the difficulties of trying to convert complex conceptions of poverty into useful statistical data.

- Alternatively we might conceive of poverty as *social exclusion*, in which case we would want indicators showing people's participation in different aspects of society and the extent to which they have economic, social and political rights. Solutions are likely to focus on tackling the mechanisms and relationships which enforce exclusion. These may well include improving individuals' capabilities as well as trying to change the way social structures (e.g. gender and class relations) and institutions (e.g. banks, schools, markets, health services) operate so that they help rather than hinder the poor.

- Clearly, the nearer we move towards a *relational view* of poverty, the more difficult it is to capture the essence of it in statistics because relationships are difficult to quantify. This is why qualitative analysis is so useful. Nevertheless numerical data can be useful in identifying some of the inequalities that are the concern of relational approaches, such as the distribution of income (see Section 6.3 below).

Box 5.1 HDI and HPI

The Human Development Index and Human Poverty Index are defined in the Course Book, p.16. They reflect the UNDP's attempts to define and measure poverty in a broader way than the traditional income approach favoured by the World Bank.

The HDI is an average measure of health, education and income for a *whole* society. By contrast, the HPI only measures the *condition of the poor* in a society and so provides policy-makers at the macro level with a more refined basis than the HDI on which to devise pro-poor policies.

5.3 The process of using poverty data

You have already done a lot of statistical work in *Preparing for Development*, the Course Book and *Study Guide 1* (ranking data, trends over time, pie charts to show percentage shares, bar charts showing comparisons and scatter diagrams showing the relationship between pairs of variables). I now want to take you through a *process* of data handling so that you understand the sort of decisions involved at each stage. This should help you not only to handle data more competently yourself but also to evaluate how others manage the process.

Using poverty data involves three steps:

1   deciding which data to use

2   deciding how to organize the data

3   interpreting the data.

Of course, unless you are doing primary research, you will have to use statistics collected by others which may not be exactly in the form you need.

In order to focus our thoughts, let's take a specific issue. In Chapter 4 of the Course Book, Parker and Wilson note the importance of female education in promoting good health generally. If you were faced with the problem of what policies to adopt to reduce HIV/AIDS among poor people, it would be useful to know whether there are data to support the *generalization* that female education reduces the likelihood of HIV/AIDS infection. This generalization conceptualizes poverty as ignorance or lack of knowledge which causes the spread of HIV. (We could also say that the generalization conceptualizes poverty as ill health, in which case we have one aspect of poverty causing another.)

Now we are going to take the three steps noted above to try and use statistical data to throw light on this problem.

1   *Deciding which data to use*

Concepts of poverty, especially the more abstract ones such as 'vulnerability', 'participation' or 'female autonomy' do not always translate easily into measurable indicators and we have to use *proxies*, i.e. indicators that approximate to the ones we want to measure. When looking at any set of data, therefore, you should ask what it is *actually* measuring and what it is *trying* to measure – they may not be very close!

We have two concepts in our question: 'female education' and 'HIV/ AIDS infection'. Does 'female' refer to girls or women? And does 'education' refer to primary, secondary or tertiary education? Or do we want to take a broader view and look at literacy rates on the assumption that literacy and education are not necessarily synonymous? In terms of this particular issue, I have chosen 'women' on the basis that they are likely to be more sexually active than girls. And I have chosen 'literacy' as I think it may be more important than levels of formal education in making women aware of HIV and its prevention. Even so, we should note that literacy is often difficult to determine.

'HIV/AIDS infection' is a clearer concept but we may assume that the statistics tend to underestimate the real incidence due to lack of diagnosis and/or reluctance to admit to the problem. (Until very recently, for example, China officially maintained that it had no HIV infection.)

2 *Deciding how to organize the data*

Since we are trying to see if there is any relationship between two variables, we need to use the data so that we can see any relationship as clearly as possible. Displaying the data in a raw form as in Table 5.3 below doesn't enable us to see easily if there is any pattern, so it's far better to use the scatter diagram[*] in Figure 5.2.

[*]Instructions on how to draw a scatter diagram are provided in Preparing for Development.

Table 5.3 Data for two variables (%)

	People living with HIV/AIDS aged 15–49	Female literacy aged 15+
	1997	*1998*
Philippines	0.06	94.6
China	0.06	74.6
Sri Lanka	0.07	88.3
Algeria	0.07	54.3
Jamaica	0.09	89.9
Pakistan	0.09	28.9
Chile	0.20	95.2
Mexico	0.35	88.7
Malaysia	0.62	82.0
Brazil	0.63	84.5
India	0.82	43.5
Thailand	2.23	93.2
Ghana	2.38	59.9
Nigeria	4.12	52.5
Tanzania	9.42	64.3
Uganda	9.51	54.2
Kenya	11.64	73.5
South Africa	12.91	83.9
Namibia	19.94	79.7
Botswana	25.10	78.2

Source: UNDP (2000) *Human Development Report*, Oxford University Press, New York, pp.190–193, 255–258.

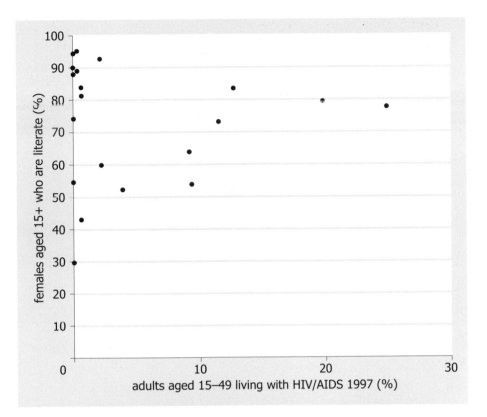

Figure 5.2 Scatter diagram of HIV/AIDS and female literacy.

3   *Interpreting the data*

When interpreting a scatter diagram, it's often useful to start by asking what you would expect it to look like if it were providing strong evidence for or against the generalization you are trying to test. In this case, we would expect, in support, a strong negative correlation: that is, as female literacy rises, HIV/AIDS falls. Such a clear pattern is not discernible here, which makes interpretation difficult. (This is often the case with scatter diagrams but it is important not to be unnerved by it and not to try and force the data to say something they don't.) We could call it a very weak negative correlation because there is a heavy cluster in the top-left corner (high literacy and low HIV) with a wide scatter drifting down to the right (lower literacy and higher HIV). When points are as scattered as these it is often difficult to see outliers, let alone use them to ask further questions.

We should also note that our sample contains only 20 countries. We might have got a clearer picture with a larger sample, but not necessarily so. In general, though, the larger the sample, the more reliable the picture that emerges.

Our diagram, then, doesn't seem to give much support, if any, to our generalization. Even if there were a very weak negative correlation, this would indicate that there must be other factors (often qualitative) which might explain the prevalence of HIV, such as cultural attitudes to promiscuity, male attitudes to condom use, women's subordination generally, health education, general health levels, and so on. Some of these variables may in turn be associated with low incomes or lack of provision of adequate and accessible healthcare services. But remember that, even if our diagram gave strong support, we couldn't use it to *prove* that female literacy causes a reduction in HIV. Correlations indicate an apparent relationship between variables and the strength of that relationship but they can't prove or explain cause and effect.

Summary of Section 5

Now let's sum up the main points of this section.

- Measuring poverty can be difficult due to:

  problems of collecting reliable and comparable statistics;

  problems of trying to translate such a complex concept into measurable indicators.

- The interpretation of statistical data is not simply a matter of looking at relationships between numbers but of probing the conceptual assumptions behind the chosen indicators.

- Quantitative data enable us to see patterns of poverty, or different dimensions of poverty, both statically and over time, which can be useful in formulating and monitoring policies to help the poor.

- Quantitative data cannot tell us *why* poverty occurs. In order to understand that, we have to find qualitative evidence (such as the role of gender attitudes in the spread of HIV, in the example above).

6 Poverty and inequality

Now that we've explored how different conceptions of poverty might be used in analysing and measuring it, let's add to our toolkit by exploring briefly two concepts which are closely related both to each other and to different views of what can be done about poverty: inequality and social justice.

6.1 Inequality and social justice

Inequality is raised as a problem at various points in the Course Book, notably in relation to access to food, clean water, health provision and information technology (Chapters 3, 4, 19 and 20). Increasing inequality, both within and between countries, is also noted to be a result of globalization (Chapters 15 and 16).

What is inequality? This is a much debated philosophical question which has thrown up many complex arguments and considerable disagreements. Amartya Sen has long been concerned not only with issues of poverty but with those of social justice, in which conceptions of inequality play a central role. And since we have already used his conception of poverty I think it will be useful also to look at his related conception of inequality (Sen, 1995).

The central question for Sen is 'equality of what?'. The answer can, of course, cover all sorts of factors such as income, wealth, resources, rights, capabilities and so on (although we are not, of course, talking about perfect equality). Sen's choice, not surprisingly, is equality of *freedom* to achieve capabilities (means) *and* actual achievement of capabilities (ends). Sen says that his question 'equality of what?' is crucial for two reasons:

- First, we need an answer if we are going to analyse and assess inequality.
- Second, different views of social justice tend to vary largely in their response to this question.

Let's look at each of these aspects in turn.

First, in order to analyse inequality we have to distinguish between equality of means and equality of outcomes. Sen argues that this is vital because all men and women are *not* created equal; there are huge differences in people's natural abilities and social circumstances. If we focus only on equality of means, we ignore these differences and end up entrenching inequalities rather than ameliorating them. For this reason, Sen criticizes ideas of social justice based on promoting specific equal opportunities (means) such as the provision of equal incomes. Instead, he argues that if we want (roughly) equal outcomes this will entail some *inequality* of means due to the differences between people, So, for example, pupils who are less able at a subject need more teaching than the more able pupils if the gap between them (i.e. in their capabilities) is to be closed.

We can't, therefore, have equality in all aspects of life. For example, equal freedom to engage in markets for jobs, land or any other commodity will result in some inequalities of outcome as some gain more than others while some may lose out altogether. This means that conflicts can and do arise as to which particular aspect(s) of inequality ought to concern us, what should be done about them and what the consequences are likely to be.

This brings us to Sen's second point that different conceptions of equality reflect different views of social justice. Social justice refers to the morally defensible distribution of material and non-material benefits and rewards in society. Conceptions of social justice can broadly be divided into those which favour equality of means and those which favour equality of outcomes. We are now going to look briefly at the views of two influential contemporary philosophers who exemplify these contrasting conceptions.

Equality of means

Robert Nozick (1974) bases his conception of social justice on the principle that everyone should have equal rights and freedom of choice:

> Individuals have rights, and there are things no person or group may do to them (without violating their rights).

> (Nozick, 1974, p.ix)

Nozick's concern with equal and inviolable rights leads him to argue that people are entitled to keep whatever goods they hold (including money) provided that they were either:

1   justly acquired in so far as nobody held them before; or

2   justly transferred (e.g. as gifts, profits, inherited wealth, interest on loans, etc.) from someone entitled to the holding to someone else by mutual choice or agreement;

and if goods are held unjustly there must be a system for rectifying the injustice.

Nozick, therefore, is concerned only about the *way* in which individuals acquire goods. He is not concerned about equal distribution of outcomes for societies. Indeed, his system precludes any such outcome and, he argues, attempts by the state to impose it are unjust:

> Our main conclusions about the state are that a minimal state, limited to the narrow functions of protection against force, theft, fraud, enforcement of contracts, and so on, is justified; that any more extensive

state will violate persons' rights not to be forced to do certain things, and this is unjustified; and that the minimal state is inspiring as well as right.

(Nozick, 1974, p.ix)

You have come across this view of the minimalist role of the state before in the discussion of neoliberalism (Course Book, ch.2).

Equality of outcomes

John Rawls wrote his theory of justice in reaction to the utilitarian principle of 'the greatest happiness for the greatest number' which inevitably sacrifices the happiness (or needs) of the minority to those of the majority. A good example of this view was the statement once made by Norman Lamont, a British Conservative Chancellor of the Exchequer, that unemployment was 'a price well worth paying' for keeping inflation low.

By contrast, Rawls wanted to establish a system of justice which would benefit rather than exclude the least well-off. He argues that if we were all asked to devise principles for a fair distribution of goods and rewards without knowing what positions we would hold in society, we would tend to ensure that we would maximize what we would get if we ended up in the worst position. So, for example, we might decide that doctors and refuse collectors should have fairly similar incomes as we don't know which job we might have.

Rawls believes that the following conception of justice would emerge from this hypothetical exercise:

> All social values – liberty and opportunity, income and wealth, and the basis of self-respect – are to be distributed equally unless an unequal distribution of any, or all, of these values is to everyone's advantage.

(Rawls, 1971, p.62)

Let's unpack the main elements of this statement:

- The 'social values' he also calls 'social primary goods', that is to say, 'things that every rational man [sic] is presumed to want' (p.62). He distinguishes these *social* primary goods, such as income, health care and education, from *natural* primary goods such as physical ability, intelligence, talent and so on. But his definition of justice is concerned only with the distribution of *social* goods.

- 'Liberty' in Rawls' sense refers not to a general principle such as Nozick's, but to the narrower sense of political and civil liberties (e.g. the right to vote and stand for election; freedom of speech, thought and assembly; freedom from arbitrary arrest and so on).

- Rawls' point about distribution is that inequalities are permissible but only if everyone's position is improved by them. So, for example, it might be worth paying some people more than others if their contributions to society (e.g. to medical research or economic growth) can benefit everyone.

Rawls' emphasis on equal civil and political liberties is uncontentious but his arguments in favour of equal distribution of income, wealth and opportunity have come in for criticism from, among others, Sen and Nozick.

While Sen is sympathetic to Rawls' idea of justice as a fair distribution of goods and values, he criticizes Rawls' emphasis on means – that is, everyone having an equal bundle of *social* primary goods to start off with, as this would consolidate inequality of outcomes due to the *natural* differences between people:

> If the object is to concentrate on the individual's real opportunity to pursue her objectives (as Rawls explicitly recommends), then account would have to be taken not only of the primary goods the persons respectively hold, but also of the relevant personal characteristics that govern the *conversion* of primary goods into the person's ability to promote her ends. For example, a person who is disabled may have a larger basket of primary goods and yet have less chance to lead a normal life (or to pursue her objectives) than an able-bodied person with a smaller basket of primary goods. Similarly, an older person or a person more prone to illness can be more disadvantaged in a generally accepted sense even with a larger bundle of primary goods.
>
> (Sen, 1999, p.74)

The libertarian Nozick criticizes Rawls' conception on the grounds that it is impossible for people to have both liberty (e.g. the freedom to acquire goods they want) and to maintain a fairly equal distribution of goods or values.

Clearly, different conceptions of social justice, though often not explicit, are at the heart of different and conflicting conceptions of development. We have only been able to have the briefest look at some of the fundamental issues here but it is important to be aware of them when evaluating views of development and policies for tackling poverty. We shall pick up these issues again in Section 7.

Activity 7

Just to be sure you have understood the main arguments in the section above, try and answer the following questions then check your answers with mine in Appendix 1.

(a) What, in Sen's view, are the most important areas of equality?

(b) What is the essential difference between Rawls' and Nozick's views of social justice?

(c) What is Sen's main criticism of Rawls?

(d) What is Nozick's main criticism of Rawls?

(Spend no more than 15 minutes on this activity)

6.2 What is the relationship between poverty and inequality?

The fundamental difference between the concepts of poverty and inequality is that while poverty relates only to the poor in society (however defined), inequality covers everyone in relation to a characteristic in which the poor are deficient. So, for example, we may define the poor as all those below a certain income in a particular country, but if we wanted to know about income *inequality* we would need to know the distribution of incomes throughout the entire population from the poorest to the richest.

Nevertheless, poverty and inequality are closely related as the following activity demonstrates.

Activity 8

Read the following extract and then answer the questions below.

(Take 20 minutes to do this activity. My answers are in Appendix 1.)

> Growth is important for poverty reduction because it determines the size of the economic cake: the goods and services which are available. In poor countries, increases in the supply of income-generating resources are a necessary condition for improving entitlements to economic goods through employment and production. Without growth, it is impossible to sustain improvements in human welfare and achieve rapid poverty reduction. However, economic growth *alone* is an insufficient condition for advancing human development. Equally important is the distribution of growth: how the economic cake is divided between different groups in society (for instance, between rich and poor, or between men and women) has a critical bearing on poverty reduction.
>
> So too does another consideration: namely who participates in the baking of the cake, and on what terms. Economists often reduce social welfare questions to considerations of growth and income distribution. But the distribution of productive assets is also critical. These assets include not only what is conventionally described as physical or financial capital (land, productive inputs, savings and credit), but also human capital, for example, education and health. Both education and health are important as ends in themselves, because they enhance the quality of life and extend the range of choice for individuals. As such, they represent an important yardstick for measuring human development. However, they are equally important as means to the end of economic growth and equity. Higher levels of education and better health enable poor people to contribute more fully to the growth process, and to participate more equitably in the opportunities which growth creates and the benefits it offers.
>
> (Watkins, 1998, p.34)

(a) What are the three important determinants of poverty reduction?

(b) How would you relate the extract to Sen's view of poverty (as failure of capabilities) and inequality? (Sections 3.2 and 6.1 above).

Watkins provides plenty of evidence for the relationship between growth, poverty and inequality. A few examples must suffice here:

- Despite a considerable rise in average per capita incomes in Pakistan between 1970 and 1990, 17 million more people fell below the poverty line and social indicators declined. Watkins blames this on 'inequalities rooted in national power structures and the debasement of political institutions' (p.36).

- In Latin America (apart from Uruguay) the growth achieved in the 1990s only benefited the richest 10% whilst the poorest 40% saw their share of national income stagnate or decline (pp.36–37).

- By contrast, Malaysia, having had strong growth with increasing income inequality until 1970, then adopted a new policy stressing equality and poverty reduction. The result was that the percentage of the total population below the poverty line fell from 60% to about 18% and the income share of the poorest 20% rose by one-third between 1973 and 1987 (pp.40–41).

The World Bank provides further support for Watkins' contention that inequality inhibits poverty reduction:

Figure 6.1 Images of inequality: pavement dwellers living next to skyscrapers in Bombay, 1997.

Other things being the same, growth leads to less poverty reduction in unequal societies than in egalitarian ones. If poor people get a small share of existing income and if inequality is unchanged, they will also get a small share of the new income generated by growth, muting the effects of growth on poverty. Evidence confirms this: when initial inequality is low, growth reduces poverty nearly twice as much as when inequality is high.

Initial inequality in income is not the whole story – for inequality in other dimensions matters too. The sensitivity of poverty to growth depends a great deal on initial inequality in poor people's access to opportunities to share in this growth. If disparities in educational attainment mirror disparities in income, poor people may not have the skills to find employment in dynamic and growing sectors of the economy. This effect is compounded by gender inequality in access to education.

(World Bank, 2000/2001, p.55)

Issues of poverty and inequality are not only relevant to developing countries. In Britain, one of the richest countries in the world, a recent study by the Joseph Rowntree Foundation argues that thousands of people die prematurely each year as a result of neoliberal government policies in the late 1970s and 1980s that increased unemployment, child poverty and inequalities of income and wealth (Mitchell *et al.* 2000).

If we accept Alan Thomas's view that 'development is now thought of mostly in terms of ameliorating problems rather than searching for alternative modes of wholesale social transformation' (Course Book, p.10), then we accept that development will take place for the foreseeable future within the capitalist system. That system is concerned with growth but not with equal outcomes and may exacerbate both inequality and poverty if left unrestrained. So if poverty is to be reduced, interventions will be necessary to redistribute whatever factors seem most appropriate. This might mean progressive taxation, public provisioning, land redistribution, unemployment benefits, food subsidies or any other mechanisms to 'govern the market' in order to ensure that the poor get more of what they need and want.

6.3 Measuring inequalities within countries

If, as evidence in Section 6.2 seems to show, inequalities seem to exacerbate poverty, we need to be able to identify the nature and extent of inequalities within societies if we are to tackle them and, by implication, poverty.

As we have seen, inequality may be characterized in all sorts of ways, ranging from incomes to a variety of social and other economic indicators. The picture can be further enriched by comparing inequalities in specific factors between, say, men and women or different occupations or ethnic groups and so on.

The World Bank uses two indicators to measure the distribution of income within countries. For the purposes of this Introduction you don't need to know how to construct them but you should be able to understand what they mean as you will often come across them in discussions on inequality.

Percentage share of income

This indicator of income inequality divides the population up into the richest tenth (decile) or fifth (quintile), the next richest decile or quintile and so on. Then the income of each decile or quintile is calculated as a percentage of the national income. Table 6.1 gives some examples. Simply read across the table for each country to see how the income is unequally shared between the quintiles.

The Gini index

The Gini index measures the extent to which the distribution of income between individuals or households deviates from a perfectly equal

Table 6.1 Percentage share of income by households and Gini index in selected countries

	Lowest 20%	Second 20%	Third 20%	Fourth 20%	Highest 20%	Gini index
Denmark	9.6	14.9	18.3	22.7	34.5	24.7
Poland	9.3	13.8	17.7	22.6	36.6	27.2
Bangladesh	9.4	13.5	17.2	22.0	37.9	28.3
Sri Lanka	8.9	13.1	16.9	21.7	39.3	30.1
China	5.5	9.8	14.9	22.3	47.5	41.5
Kenya	5.0	9.7	14.2	20.9	50.2	44.5
Russian Federation	4.2	8.8	13.6	20.7	52.8	48.0
Malaysia	4.6	8.3	13.0	20.4	53.7	48.4
Nicaragua	4.2	8.0	12.6	20.0	55.2	50.3
Chile	3.5	6.6	10.9	18.1	61.0	56.5
Zimbabwe	4.0	6.3	10.0	17.4	62.3	56.8
South Africa	2.9	5.5	9.2	17.7	64.8	59.3
Brazil	2.5	5.7	9.9	17.7	64.2	60.1
Sierra Leone	1.1	2.0	9.8	23.7	63.4	62.9

Source: World Bank (1999/2000) *World Development Report*, Oxford University Press, New York, table 4 (data cover various years from 1989 to 1996).

distribution. A Gini index of 0 represents perfect equality while 100 represents perfect inequality (i.e. the hypothetical situation of one person or household having all the country's income). When reading a Gini index, therefore, you need to bear in mind that the higher it is, the more unequal the income distribution. Table 6.1 also shows the Gini index for each country. The index incorporates the income shares data to show the overall extent of inequality.

Activity 9

From your course reading and general knowledge you might like to think about possible reasons for the variations between countries in Table 6.1. For example, why do you think Sri Lanka has much less income inequality than the Russian Federation, South Africa and Brazil? (You might get some clues from the Course Book, section 4.4.)

(Don't spend more than 10 minutes on this and then have a look at my answers in Appendix 1.)

As we noted in Section 5.2 above, data on inequalities within countries (or communities or households) are useful for analysing poverty from a relational viewpoint. In 1995 the UNDP introduced two new composite measures in its Human Development Report: the Gender Development Index (GDI) and the Gender Empowerment Measure (GEM) (UNDP, 1995). The GDI measures the same dimensions as the HDI (life expectancy, adult literacy rates and per capita incomes) but takes account of inequalities between men and women. The GEM measures women's participation in political decision-making, their access to professional opportunities and their earning power. The GDI, like the HDI, measures endowments, whereas the GEM measures how they are transformed into capabilities by women to achieve in the economic and political spheres. The GEM may, therefore, be regarded as a measure of entitlement or, conversely, social exclusion.

Activity 10

Have a look at Table 6.2, where the countries are ranked in order of GDP *per capita*. Now rank the countries according to their GEM, starting with the highest (the lower the GEM values, the greater the gender inequality in key areas of the economy and politics). What strikes you about the result?

(Only spend 10 minutes on this)

Table 6.2 Gender inequality and income for selected countries

	GDP per capita (US$ PPP 1998)	GEM
Japan	23 257	0.490
Ireland	21 482	0.593
Italy	20 585	0.524
Spain	16 212	0.615
Portugal	14 701	0.618
Greece	13 943	0.456
South Korea	13 478	0.323
Chile	8787	0.440

Source: UNDP (2000) *Human Development Report*, Oxford University Press, New York, pp.157–158, 165–166.

Comment

What strikes me is that for this particular selection of countries there is no clear relationship between income levels and gender equality. Japan stands out especially with the highest incomes but with a GEM far lower than many poorer countries. The lesson to be drawn from this is that gender equality is not dependent on economic development and that culture and public policy are likely to be important influences on women's opportunities.

6.4 Measuring inequalities between countries

McGrew (Course Book, p.353) points out that 'whilst the relationship between globalization and world poverty is enormously complicated, there is general acknowledgement that globalization is strongly associated with an intensification of global inequality.'

Section 4.2 on international aspects of poverty highlighted some of the international mechanisms and processes which contribute towards current economic and political inequalities between countries.

International inequalities can be measured by comparing countries in terms of all sorts of variables such as Internet access (Table 4.2 above), shares of manufactured exports, shares of foreign direct investment (Table 4.1 above), per capita incomes and social indicators such as number of people per doctor, or educational enrolments (as in Table 4.3 above). The HDI, as we saw earlier, tries to capture both income and social indicators.

Income comparisons can be done quite simply by comparing GNP per capita between countries, groups of countries or regions. For example, see Table 6.3. Note that both columns measure GNP per capita but the second one is measured at 'purchasing power parity'* although if you rank the two columns you will see only a small difference between them.

*PPP is defined in the Course Book, box 1.3, p.12.

Table 6.3 Regional differences in average incomes

	GNP per capita (US$ 1998)	GNP per capita (US$ at PPP 1998)
East Asia and Pacific	990	3400
East Europe and Central Asia	2190	4240
Latin America and Caribbean	3940	6780
Middle East and North Africa	2050	4220
South Asia	430	1610
Sub-Saharan Africa	480	1430
High income countries	25 510	23 440

Source: World Bank (1999/2000) *World Development Report*, Oxford University Press, New York, table 1.

The main problem with the above data set is that the regional headings hide great differences between countries within each region. For example, within East Asia and Pacific, in 1998 the GNP per capita of Japan was $32 380 while that of Cambodia was $280.

Table 6.3 gives us a static picture of the situation in 1998. Table 6.4 below gives a more dynamic view of what's been happening to inter-country incomes over a long period. Of course, it only gives us two comparators – the richest and the poorest countries – and it doesn't tell us which they are. Nor are they likely to be exactly the same countries in each year. But you could still use the same idea to look at ratios between individual countries or groups of specified countries. Note that the gap has increased steadily over nearly two hundred years and that the biggest gap has occurred during the last thirty.

Table 6.4 Ratio of incomes per capita between richest and poorest countries

Year	1820	1913	1950	1973	1992
Ratio[a]	3 to 1	11 to 1	35 to 1	44 to 1	72 to 1

[a]That is, the per capita incomes of the richest countries were, for example as in 1820, three times greater than those in poor countries.

Source: UNDP (1999) *Human Development Report*, Oxford University Press, New York, p.38.

Summary of Section 6

Now we can sum up the main points of this section as follows:

- Inequality is a complex and contested concept and arguments about it lie at the heart of debates about social justice and development policy.

- Poverty is different from but related to inequality since poverty is usually a manifestation of inequality and can be exacerbated by it.

- Quantifying inequalities both within and between countries can provide evidence of the extent and nature of inequality, but can't explain why it occurs.

7 Evaluating proposals for tackling poverty

There is obviously widespread concern and a lot of ideas about what can be done about poverty but, as I said at the beginning, we are not contributing solutions here. Instead we are going to use what we have learned to see how we might evaluate policy proposals for reducing poverty.

7.1 Causes of poverty

Suggestions for tackling poverty are usually based on some idea of what causes it. In terms of the conceptual frameworks we looked at earlier, for example, we could ask what causes social exclusion or failure of capabilities. These concepts cover many areas of human existence, as we have seen. Moreover, one aspect of poverty is likely to be related to several others so our question is very complex. We are going to focus on one particular (but still quite complex) aspect of poverty and see how we might explore the question: what causes poverty?

Before we do so, let me remind you about a very important point that the authors of *Study Guide 1* make in Section 4. In relation to the causes of famine, they extract two explanations, both based on Sen's work, from the Course Book (Chapter 3). Famines occur because:

- entitlements are made vulnerable (capability failure); and
- where the poor have little political clout, governments don't feel obliged to prevent famine and are not held to account for that failure (political exclusion of the poor).

As the authors point out, *the identification of these causes of famine suggests strategies for action.* If you agree that these are the likely causes of famine, then the solution is to improve livelihoods by maintaining entitlements and to ensure effective political representation of the poor, although all that's easier said than done.

If, on the other hand, you agree with the third generalization in Chapter 3 (p.60) that famine is caused by a failure of food supply, you would be more likely to argue that the solution should be to increase food production and/or food imports (also easier said than done). Of course, you may feel that improving aggregate food supplies is a good idea in conjunction with the other policies suggested above.

Before Sen did his research, the *accepted conception* of famine was that it was due to insufficient overall supplies of food. But when Sen *measured* food availability in famine areas, he found that there was not an aggregate shortfall and that the rich never starved. This led him to *analyse* the causes in terms of economic and political relationships which led him to a *new conception* of famine as failure of entitlements.

Now we are going to analyse another aspect of poverty and see what complications might arise when we ask what can be done about it.

Activity 11

Use the Course Book Chapter 6 'Is the world overpopulated?' to answer the following questions:

(a) What are the three main views in Chapter 6.2 on the relationship between poverty and population growth?

(b) What poverty reduction strategies are suggested by each view?

(c) Do you think the strategies are mutually exclusive?

(d) Can you relate any of the views on poverty and population to social exclusion, failure of capabilities or relational poverty?

(Spend about 30 minutes on this activity. You can compare your answers with mine in Appendix 1.)

I want to draw out some general points from the analyses of famine and population that we've just looked at. These points would also be applicable to the other analyses of particular poverty issues in the Course Book, i.e. on disease, unemployment, environmental degradation and war.

The lessons that I have learned from studying these issues are:

■ the difficulty sometimes of establishing what is cause and what is effect (especially true in the population example since poverty may well cause people to have lots of children, but having lots of children puts a strain on the resources of poor households);

■ that any particular solution depends on what is perceived to be the cause(s);

■ that proposed solutions are not merely technical (though they may appear to be) but reflect, implicitly or explicitly, the values and interests of those proposing them;

■ that even apparently contrary solutions may both be useful in any particular context;

■ that in the analytical and ideological worlds, issues and debates tend to get polarized and simplified but the real world is a lot more messy and complex.

7.2 Public action

Asking 'what can be done about poverty?' puts the question in the passive mode, thereby avoiding a very important question: *who* is doing the doing? The simple answer is that it might be all sorts of people, groups and institutions, so we might have to look at different levels of public action or some combination of them.

In Activity 1 we asked to whom poverty might matter. The answers gave us some idea of the range of institutions and interests which might be affected by poverty directly and indirectly. But we can't assume that their responses to it will be benign or, if benign, effective. Some responses, especially by repressive governments, might be to attack or ignore the poor. Others, such as NGOs, might not listen to the poor and so implement inappropriate solutions. Others might say that they are acting on behalf of the poor but be perceived as acting on behalf of the rich (an accusation often flung at the World Bank, the IMF and the WTO).

Drèze and Sen (1989) argue that the amelioration of poverty by public action is only likely to occur if:

1   the poor participate in the process of public action to articulate their needs;

2   poverty (in whatever form) is widely accepted as a public concern requiring public action in the interests of the poor;

3   the providers of public goods are accountable to the poor or, at least, responsive to their needs.

Unfortunately there are often in-built problems with this ideal scenario.

Activity 12

(a)   What might prevent poor people from participating in public action and articulating their needs?

(b)   Why might it be difficult for the interests of the poor to become accepted as a focus for public action to meet their needs?

(c)   Why might those with the ability to provide public goods not be accountable to the poor?

(Spend 10 minutes answering these questions)

Comment

(a)   There might be several aspects to this answer and they may be interconnected. Poor people tend not to be very literate (and women less than men) so writing to newspapers (if there is a free press) or to their parliamentary representatives (if they have them) might be impossible. People with little or no education usually end up working extremely hard with little time to engage in public action. This is particularly true of women who, the world over, tend to do 'double work', contributing to their household income and bearing the brunt of all the domestic labour. In addition, in many societies it is culturally unacceptable for women to engage in the public sphere.

(b)   As I said earlier, public action is not necessarily directed at meeting the needs of the poor. There are lots of other interests jostling for their own ends in the public arena and these ends may be directly opposed to the interests of the poor. Richer taxpayers may object strongly to public money being spent on reducing poverty, especially if the poor are blamed for their own situation. Public debates on poverty usually contain implicit or explicit references to morality which may be used to support public action for the poor ('it is right to do so') but may be equally used to oppose such action on the grounds that the poor are idle, dependent, irresponsible about contraception, ignorant and so on.

(c) Those most likely to provide public goods are governments, international NGOs and international institutions such as the World Bank. The latter two are not accountable either to the poor or to their elected representatives (Course Book, pp.204, 213). Authoritarian regimes are, by definition, unaccountable to anyone, but nor is there any guarantee that democratically elected governments will be accountable to the poor even if they make up the bulk of the population. David Potter cites the example of India (Course Book, p.377): 'At the end of the twentieth century, India had the largest number of desperately poor people in the world – between 370 and 390 million or about 40% of India's total population. Most of the rural poor were landless peasants, and landlessness was a major cause of their poverty. India had been a liberal democracy for 50 years, with political leaders like Nehru and others publicly committed to eradicating poverty. Efforts at land reform to benefit the poor were attempted, but liberal democratic political processes enabled powerful landed (conservative) élites to ensure that land reform legislation in the states of India did not radically affect their interests. Liberal democracy also enabled the poor to vote, but periodic elections were too blunt an instrument to affect the power of the landed élites.'

This raises an interesting question about the point Drèze and Sen make about the importance of public pressure on the Indian government in the prevention of famine (Course Book, box 3.3, p.63). If Indian governments are so responsive to the fear of potential famine, why have they failed to tackle poverty effectively in other ways?

Whatever the relationship between democracy and development, and it is highly contested (Course Book, chapter 17), I think we can take it as axiomatic that, unless the poor have champions among the influential, they are likely to be their own best advocates in trying to tackle poverty. Let's have a brief look at an important but contested concept that seeks to capture the processes by which the poor may be able to ensure that their needs are met.

7.3 Empowerment

Empowerment is defined in the Course Book as 'a desired process by which individuals, typically including the 'poorest of the poor', are to take direct control over their lives. Once 'empowered' to do so, poor people will then (hopefully) be able to be the agents of their own development' (p.35). This view reflects conceptions of poverty as both failure of capabilities, social exclusion and relational, as we shall see.

The etymological kernel of 'empowerment' is 'power' (not surprisingly yet another contested concept) so we need to tackle that idea first.* We often speak of power as if it were some personal attribute or ability as in, for example, describing someone as powerful or saying that someone has the power to do something. By contrast, power can be viewed essentially as the expression of an unequal relationship between individuals, groups, classes, countries, etc.

*The concept of power is discussed at greater length in *Study Guide 1*, section 10.

Empowerment, based on these views of power, can therefore mean either:

- people acquiring the ability to do something they otherwise couldn't do; or

- altering power relationships so that one group is no longer subordinate to another.

Activity 13

Turn to p.35 of the Course Book and answer the following questions:

(a) In terms of the two alternatives posed above, how do you think Schumacher and Korten view empowerment?

(b) Comment on their views in terms of structure and agency.

(Spend 15 minutes on this activity)

Comment

Schumacher talks about what can be done by people themselves, with the implication of self-reliance in order to meet their material needs. This accords with a view of empowerment as enhancing capabilities (which might remind you of Sen's view of development). It also stresses agency.

Korten, on the other hand, calls for, among other things, the redistribution of power and transformation of institutions. This more closely reflects the view of empowerment as involving structural changes to alter power relationships (a relational view of poverty).

The two views are not mutually exclusive and it may be that enhancing people's capabilities also facilitates any attempts they might want to make to alter structural relationships. The following extract illustrates the point. It is from an interview with Irene Soto, a Mexican woman organizer in the National Council of the Urban Popular Movement in Mexico:

> A lot of women begin participating in the organization by engaging in the simplest activity. They just go to meetings. For them, just leaving the four walls of their home is a big deal. A lot of the women who come to the meeting for the first time tell us 'I can't come any more because my husband won't let me.' Others say, 'Well, I come to these meetings because I need to figure out how to solve my economic problems, even though my husband doesn't approve of me being here.' When women say they are going to come despite what their husbands do, it makes some of the other women question their own situation. They begin to ask, 'Why can't I decide to leave my house and come to a meeting in the neighbourhood?' They start to question things at home.
>
> (Stephen, 1997, p.151)

Empowerment is often seen as a particularly important process for poor women who are disadvantaged by both their class and their gender. Understanding their position entails taking a relational view of poverty so as to see how social structures and institutions foster and maintain gender inequalities. Kabeer (1994, p.225) points out, for example, that studies of the household division of labour 'highlighted the extent to which the assignment of domestic responsibilities to women is so deeply institutionalized in household rules and practices that it appears non-negotiable. Women who wish to take up employment can only do so by cutting down on their leisure or withdrawing children from school. They rarely do so by renegotiating the division of labour so that husbands undertake a greater share of domestic chores. Similarly, while women may successfully bargain over certain aspects of household expenditure, what remains non-negotiable is men's overall control over household land, capital and other valued resources.'

So what can be done to empower the poor and especially poor women? Kabeer uses studies of several NGOs working with women in poor countries to draw some important conclusions about 'empowerment from below' especially to tackle social exclusion. If they are to have any chance of success, NGOs must:

- Ensure that women are active participants both in identifying their needs and interests and in deciding how to meet them.

- Compensate for institutional failures which exclude women: for example, the Grameen Bank in Bangladesh, set up to provide women with credit because they lacked collateral to borrow from conventional banks; and the Self Employed Women's Association (SEWA) in India, set up because conventional trades unions were run by men and oriented to their needs. Both of these organizations have moved beyond their original remits as their women members have further defined their own needs.

- Help women to be critical of the *status quo* and to see new possibilities, what Kabeer calls strategies of 'empowerment from within': 'New forms of consciousness arise out of women's newly acquired access to the intangible resources of analytical skills, social networks, organizational strength, solidarity and sense of not being alone' (pp.245–246).

- And, related to the last point in the quotation, recognize the importance of collective identity and action so that women realize that:

  they share their subordination;

  subordination is not inevitable;

  their own organizational solidarity can help to compensate for their exclusion from other sources of institutional power and provide a base from which to challenge oppressive social structures and processes (Figure 7.1).

Empowerment strategies are part of public action and, like all forms of public action, they are part of a process which can be difficult and unpredictable for the following reasons:

Figure 7.1 Collective empowerment: Brazilian women of the Landless Rural Workers' Movement (Movimento Sem Terra) demand equal rights in land reform, health, social security and job opportunities, Brasilia 2000.

- While many development NGOs are committed to empowerment, the meaning they attach to the term and their objectives in promoting it need to be interrogated.

- Altering power relationships is usually extremely difficult for the simple reason that those in the dominant position, whatever the basis of their power (land, money, gender, etc.), will be reluctant to lose it and may become violent against those who seek to undermine their position.

- It is also true, as Sen (1999) has pointed out, that many unequal structural relationships survive on the basis of 'co-operative conflict' because each party has something to gain from the arrangement. So, for example, women in highly male-dominated societies may feel vulnerable without traditional male protection and so be reluctant to try and reduce their subordination.

- Finally, we must not assume that people's desire for empowerment, however defined, necessarily means that they are seeking equality with others. They may wish to be empowered in order to have power over others.

The concept of empowerment is intrinsically bound up with the idea that the poor should determine their own lives on the basis of their experience and aspirations. This idea will be explored further in Part 2.

7.4 Conflicting views on poverty and development

> Moral philosophy sets the background for, and the boundaries of, political philosophy.
>
> (Nozick, 1974, p.6)

Nozick's observation reminds us that different views of social justice are important determinants of political action. We saw this in the first two chapters of the Course Book where a fundamental ideological tension runs through the discussion of poverty and development. Essentially, the conflict is between those who believe that free markets and economic growth are the answer to poverty (neoliberals) and those who argue that, while growth is important, its effects may be detrimental to the poor and exacerbate inequalities, necessitating some form of socialism (structuralists) or considerable state intervention (interventionists).

Thomas seems to resolve this tension by arguing that neoliberalism and structuralism 'are largely discredited. Instead, the main question within 'mainstream' development is about the degree and form of *interventionism. People-centred development* may provide an alternative.' (p.48).

I think that Thomas is right about the current views in mainstream development and it is certainly true that socialist models of development have taken a thrashing (at least for the moment) and that a lot of structuralists have slipped into the interventionist camp. But we shouldn't infer from this that some sort of consensus exists on what should be done about poverty or about the role of markets in that process, as the following activity shows.

Activity 14

Have a look at the following extracts from recent articles and, using Thomas's Table 2.2 on p.43 of the Course Book, decide which view of development each seems to reflect.

(Spend about 15 minutes on this and then check your views against mine at the end of this text.)

Extract 1

The new intellectual fashion holds that governments should ride the globalization tiger, not try to tame it by reducing inequality. This view is short-sighted. Wealth disparities between rich and poor countries and people are not just an affront to morality. They are also a source of inefficiency and instability. And without a radical redistribution of income, the international target of halving world poverty by 2015 will be missed.

Technological change and the increased flows of trade and investment underpinning globalization are making the world richer but more unequal. In the mid-1980s, the income ratio of the poorest to the richest 5% of the world's population was 1:78. Today it is 1:123.

...Closing the gap between winners and losers at the national level demands progressive taxation and redistributive public investment in education and economic infrastructure, allied to caution in market liberalization. At an international level, income redistribution requires not just an increase in aid, but new approaches to multilateralism and market regulation. Contrary to the received wisdom, global markets are not unregulated. They are regulated to produce inequality. While the World Trade Organization demands that poor countries expose vulnerable producers to global markets, trade barriers in the north cost developing countries $700bn a year. Meanwhile, intellectual property rules designed to increase corporate profit are raising the cost of technology transfer to poor countries with devastating implications for income distribution. It is the same story in finance. Global capital markets have made east Asia's success in poverty reduction grind to a halt, while the International Monetary Fund is used to promote capital market liberalization in the interests of Wall Street. Meanwhile, corporate tax evasion through offshore centres is costing developing countries an estimated $100bn a year in lost tax revenue – more than double aid transfers.

(Watkins, 2000)

Extract 2

Critics of free trade argue that trade benefits the rich at the expense of the poor. But the evidence tells a different story. It is well-established that trade boosts economic growth. A much-quoted paper by Jeffrey Sachs and Andrew Warner of Harvard University found that developing countries with open economies grew by 4.5 per cent a year in the 1970s and 1980s, while those with closed economies grew by 0.7 per cent a year. Countless country studies support their results. But opponents of free trade retort that poor countries are still not catching up with rich ones, indeed that the rich are drawing further ahead. It is true that developing countries in general are not catching up with rich ones. Yet some are. Take South Korea. Thirty years ago it was as poor as Ghana; now it is as rich as Portugal. Or consider China, where 100m people have escaped from extreme poverty over the past decade. ...

Of course, some people do lose in the short run from trade liberalization. Some are 'fat cats' grown rich from cosy deals with governments. But others are poor farmers who lose their subsidies, or unskilled workers who lose their jobs. Their plight should not be forgotten. But the right way to alleviate the hardship of the unlucky few is through social safety nets and job retraining rather than by abandoning reforms that benefit the many.

...the surest way to do more to help the poor is to continue to open markets. And how better to do that than for governments to launch a new round of multilateral trade negotiations.

(Moore, 2000)

Summary of Section 7

We can sum up this section by saying that different people and institutions will have different and often conflicting views on what can be done about poverty depending on how they see poverty and social justice and what particular interests they represent. What is *actually* done about poverty (whether at local, national or international levels) depends on:

(a) the outcome of struggle between conflicting interests;

(b) the ability of agents to implement effective strategies.

8 Conclusion

The following is a checklist, based on this Introduction, of the basic questions you should ask when trying to evaluate any policy that claims to tackle poverty.

1   Who has been involved in drawing up and implementing the policy?

2   Whose interests do they represent?

3   What conceptions of poverty and social justice seem to inform the policy?

4   What particular aspects of poverty are being tackled and why have they been chosen?

5   Do the proposed solutions follow logically from the perceived causes?

6   What statistical data, if any, are provided to back up statements about the extent of the poverty, its causes and effects?

7   To what extent are the statistical indicators a reasonable reflection of the concept(s) of poverty in the policy?

8   Can you be confident that the statistics are accurate and reliable?

9   Is the statistical interpretation reasonable?

10 Are the quantitative data supplemented by qualitative data (case studies) to get at the reality behind the statistics, especially the impact of structural relationships (class, gender, international links, etc.)?

11 Who do you think will benefit from the policy and in what ways?

12 Who do you think might lose from it and in what ways?

Still interested?

If you want to find out more about what is actually being done about poverty from the household to the international level and you want to use and add to the skills you've gained from this Introduction by assessing different policies and forms of action on poverty, you will find plenty of stimulating material in Part 2 of *Poverty and Inequality*. This will cover three main areas:

■ The policy agendas on poverty and inequality from major development agencies and institutions. What are the similarities and differences between development agencies and what is the thinking behind their policies? How have their ideas changed and what is the significance of the international poverty targets for 2015?

- Poverty and inequality as a lived experience. This section of Part 2 will be based on case study material from households in rural India. As well as gaining an understanding about the livelihoods and daily struggles facing such households, we will look at what it means to gather data about poverty at the household level and the difficulties in interpretation. This section will thus provide you with further opportunities to hone your data handling skills.

- Types of action on poverty and inequality. In this section, we will look at the different ways that people and organizations act to try to reduce or eliminate poverty, from the everyday actions of poor people themselves to those carried out by agencies of development. This section will also provide you with a chance to develop evaluative skills, useful both for your reading and for any voluntary or work-based engagement with action on poverty and inequality.

Appendix 1: Suggested answers to activities

Activity 3

Your answers may be somewhat different from mine, which are by no means comprehensive.

Rights

(a) human: right to life, security;

(b) legal/civic: equality before the law; full and equal rights of citizenship;

(c) democratic: freedom of thought, speech and assembly; the right to participate in free and fair elections.

Resources

(a) human capital: skills and knowledge;

(b) social capital: ability and freedom of people to work together;

(c) labour markets: freedom and skills to get a job with fair pay;

(d) product markets: ability and freedom to buy and sell goods and services;

(e) state provision: fair access to state entitlements (e.g. health and education services);

(f) common property resources: access to common goods such as forest products, water, grazing land, etc.

Relationships

(a) family networks: perhaps to share production tasks and childcare, to borrow money and other needs;

(b) wider support networks: e.g. women's groups to meet practical and strategic gender needs;

(c) voluntary organizations: a more formal version of (b)? e.g. NGOs.

Activity 5

(a)

Elements of poverty in the UK	Elements of poverty in a Brazilian city
crime	no running water
prostitution	no sewage pipes
drugs	poor roads
alcoholism	fear
child abuse	violent crime
low pay and benefit cuts	illness
unemployment	high perinatal mortality
lack of skills	lack of education/illiteracy
school exclusions	drugs
failure of support networks	environmental degradation
environmental degradation	unemployment
social instability	no (legal) electricity
depression	
illness	
fear	
debt	
self-destruction	
anger	

(b) The elements of poverty seem remarkably similar considering they are in two different places, thousands of miles apart, and the articles were written by different authors. Perhaps the most shocking aspect of these accounts is that they describe such dreadful poverty in the 5th and 8th richest countries in the world (World Bank, 1999/2000, table 1).

(c) From my list, I would say the most likely *causes* of unemployment would be:

drugs

alcoholism

lack of skills

school exclusion

failure of support networks (e.g. childcare for women who want paid work)

depression

illness

And I thought the most likely *effects* of unemployment would be:

crime

prostitution

drugs

alcoholism

low income

lack of skills

social instability

depression

illness

debt

self-destruction

anger

Note that some of the causes and effects are the same!

(d) I don't think I could decide how individuals' capabilities would be affected by their poverty because capability is an individual choice, but the evidence from the extracts and my answers in (a) and (c) enables me to see how people's endowments might be adversely affected in various and connected ways.

Activity 6

(a) On income alone, the most developed would be Saudi Arabia and the least would be Sri Lanka.

(b) Judging by HDI, the most developed would be Chile and the least would be South Africa.

(c) It depends what we mean by poverty! If we mean low income, then the solution would be to increase incomes. But the tables show that income and wider aspects of well-being (health and education) are not necessarily, or always, connected. China and Sri Lanka have the lowest *per capita* incomes but their HDIs are far better than South Africa's and not far below Saudi Arabia although both these countries have far higher incomes than China and Sri Lanka.

(d) In the Course Book, Parker and Wilson (section 4.4) point out the importance of public health provision in improving Sri Lanka's health indicators and Crow (section 3.3) explains the success of the post-revolutionary Chinese state in improving the health of the population.

Activity 7

(a) Sen thinks the most important areas of equality are (i) the freedom for people to achieve their capabilities and (ii) the actual achievement of those capabilities.

(b) Nozick sees social justice as equality of means in terms of equal rights and freedom to keep the goods we acquire so long as we have gained them 'justly'. Such a principle cannot result in equality of outcomes. Rawls, by contrast, believes that social justice depends on a reasonably equitable distribution of the things we value both as means and as ends.

(c) While Sen approves of Rawls' concern about equality of outcomes, he criticizes him for thinking that this can be achieved by an equal distribution of social goods. Sen argues that, because we have different *natural* talents and characteristics, giving everyone equal means will consolidate the natural inequalities between us. Therefore, achieving equal outcomes (in whatever spheres) will almost certainly entail some inequality of material and social means, although not in political and civil liberties.

(d) Since Nozick believes that equal freedom to keep what we have is paramount, he is critical of redistributive ideas like Rawls', which, by definition, imply taking acquisitions (e.g. income or land) from the better-off and giving them to the less well-off. Hence Nozick's concern to keep the role of the state (the main agent of redistribution) to a minimum.

Activity 8

(a) According to Watkins, the three important determinants of poverty reduction are:

1 *economic growth* because it determines the size of the economy and can contribute to improvements in people's welfare;

2 *equitable distribution* of national income and productive assets;

3 *the development of human capital* (especially in terms of health and education) to enable people both to contribute to economic growth and participate in the opportunities it offers.

(b) I think that Sen would agree with Watkins that:

economic growth is a necessary but insufficient factor in improving capabilities;

grossly unequal distribution of income and other assets adversely affects the ability of poor people to achieve their potential;

participation of the poor 'in the baking of the cake' is vital if they are to benefit from growth and ensure that its fruits are equitably distributed.

Activity 9

It's not easy to provide clear answers from the little information available to us from the course but I was struck (in the Course Book, section 4.4) by the contrast between, on the one hand, Sri Lanka's low GNP per capita, good public provision and democratic tradition and, on the other, Brazil's much higher per capita income, relatively poorer public provision and weak democratic history. This suggests that Sri Lankan governments, with strong democratic support, have been able to redistribute incomes more equitably by taxation for public provision.

I would start looking for explanations for the Russian Federation's relatively high inequality in the widespread introduction of free (and often very uncontrolled) markets after the fall of the Soviet Union.

And, finally, South Africa's high inequality has its roots in the apartheid system but inequalities may well have been further exacerbated by the country's adoption of neoliberal economic policies in the 1990s.

Activity 11

(a) The three main views on the relationship between poverty and population growth are:

1   *Neo Malthusian*: that rapid population growth is a major cause of low income, economic stagnation, environmental degradation, hunger, rapid urbanization, unemployment and political instability.

2   *Social*: that rapid population growth is not a cause but a result of poverty because poor people value children's economic contribution and when the infant mortality rate is high people tend to have more children to compensate for the inevitable loss of some.

3   *Women-centred*: this overlaps with the social view but focuses particularly on the crucial role of women in reducing fertility rates.

(b) The poverty reduction strategies suggested by each view:

1   The neo-Malthusian view suggests that the answer is simply birth control since population growth causes poverty.

2   The social view suggests, on the contrary, that we need to tackle the causes of poverty directly rather than the causes of pregnancy. This would entail such policies as improving infant and child health; improving job opportunities and incomes; and providing economic security, especially for the elderly.

3   The women-centred view would also suggest such strategies to reduce poverty but would add many others related specifically to women's development, empowerment and reproductive rights. This would entail structural changes (e.g. more access for women to good health, education and employment opportunities) and especially changes in gender relations, not only with regard to fertility control and sexual practices but more generally in terms

of altering power relationships between men and women so that women have more control over all aspects of their lives.

(c) I don't think the strategies are mutually exclusive. Although (1) is completely contrary to (2) and (3) in its analysis of the relationship between poverty and population growth, there is no reason why its solution (birth control) shouldn't be promoted *alongside* the strategies suggested by (2) and (3). Indeed, we might expect easy access to reliable birth control to be an important part (but only part) of the women-centred view.

(d) I think there is some truth in the view that rapid population growth (whatever its cause) is likely to exacerbate poverty in the absence of equally rapid economic growth. All three views, therefore, can be related to poverty as capability failure and social exclusion. The potential of poor people, and especially women, is weakened by exclusion from education, health care, employment opportunities and so on. But the women-centred view can also be strongly linked with the relational view of poverty as it is essentially concerned with changing women's position in the social structure.

Activity 14

Extract 1

I would say that Watkins reflects a strong structuralist position in terms of his analysis. He talks of inequalities both within and between countries reflecting a relational view of poverty. He is very critical of neoliberal policies on trade and investment and criticizes the WTO for pursuing policies unfair to poor countries.

He calls for considerable intervention (progressive taxation, public investment, market regulation in favour of poor countries and so on). However, he doesn't go so far as to call for an alternative (socialist) economic system so I would put him in the 'governing the market' tent of the interventionist camp.

Extract 2

We can start by noting some intellectual confusions in the article by Moore, who is the Director-General of the WTO. First, he argues that because trade boosts economic growth, it can't be true that trade benefits the rich at the expense of the poor. He then admits that, in general, there *is* an increasing gap between rich and poor countries.

Nevertheless, he clings to trade liberalization as the solution to poverty. He clearly has a residual view of poverty ('the unlucky few' get left out of the benefits of growth) and a decidedly neoliberal view of development ('...the surest way to help the poor is to continue to open markets').

References

Allen, T. and Thomas, A. (eds.) (2000) *Poverty and Development into the 21st Century*, Oxford University Press, Oxford, in association with the Open University, Milton Keynes [Course Book].

Bernstein, H. (1992) in Bernstein, H., Crow, B. and Johnson, H. (eds) *Rural Livelihoods: Crises and Responses*, Oxford University Press, Oxford, in association with the Open University, Milton Keynes.

Drèze, J. and Sen, A. (1989) *Hunger and Public Action*, Clarendon Press, Oxford.

James, C. (1998) 'Producers welcome planned new rules on market access', *Financial Times*, 8 July.

Kabeer, N. (1994) *Reversed Realities: Gender Hierarchies in Development Thought*, Verso London.

Mitchell, R. Shaw, M. and Dorling, D. (2000) *Inequalities in Life and Death: what if Britain were more equal?*, Policy Press, Bristol.

Moore, M. (2000) 'The WTO is a friend of the poor', *Financial Times*, 19 June.

Narayan, D. *et al.* (2000) *Voices of the Poor: Can Anyone Hear Us?*, Oxford University Press, New York.

Nozick, R. (1974) *Anarchy, State and Utopia*, Blackwell Publishers, Oxford.

Rawls, J. (1971) *A Theory of Justice*, Oxford University Press, New York.

Sen, A. (1995) *Inequality Re-examined*, Oxford University Press, New York.

Sen, A. (1999) *Development as Freedom*, Oxford University Press, Oxford.

Shirazi, J.K. (1998) The East Asian Crisis: origins, policy challenges and prospects. World Bank Group Speeches, www.worldbank.org/html/extdr/asian_crisis/default.htm [accessed 17 May 2001).

Stephen, L. (1997) *Women and Social Movements in Latin America: Poverty from Below*, University of Texas Press, Austin.

UNDP (1995) *Human Development Report*, Oxford University Press, New York.

UNDP (2000) *Human Development Report: Human Rights and Human Development*, Oxford University Press, New York.

Watkins, K. (1998) *Economic Growth with Equity: Lessons from East Asia*, Oxfam GB, Oxford.

Watkins, K. (2000) 'Winners and losers and the great divide', *The Guardian*, 2 April.

World Bank (1999) *Experts call for better statistics to fight poverty* [online]. Available from: http://www.worldbank.org/html/extdr/extme/105.htm [accessed February 2001]

World Bank (1999/2000) *World Development Report*, Oxford University Press, New York.

World Bank (2000/2001) *World Development Report: Attacking Poverty*, Oxford University Press, New York.

Acknowledgements

Grateful acknowledgement is made to the following sources for permission to reproduce material within this text.

Figures

Figure 2.1: © John Harris, reportdigital.co.uk; *Figure 3.1*: © AP Photo/ Eric Draper; *Figure 4.1*: © AP Photo/Chien-min Chung; *Figure 5.1*: © 2001 The New Yorker Collection from cartoonbank.com. All Rights Reserved; *Figure 6.1*: © AP Photos/Sherwin Crasto; *Figure 7.1*: © AP Photo/Eraldo Press; *Cover photo*: © AP Photo/Carlos Eduardo.

Table

Table 4.3: From *Human Development Report 1994* by United Nations Development Programme, copyright © 1994 by United Nations Development Programme. Used by permission of Oxford University Press, Inc.

The Course Team

ACADEMIC STAFF

Joanna Chataway, *Co-Chair and author, Technology and Knowledge*

Jenny Robinson, *Co-Chair, co-ordinator and author, Displacement*

Gordon Wilson, *Co-Chair, co-ordinator and author, Sustainability*

Simon Bromley, *co-ordinator and author, Transitions*

Will Brown, *co-ordinator and author, Transitions*

Pam Furniss, *author, Sustainability*

Tom Hewitt, *co-ordinator and author, Technology and Knowledge*

Hazel Johnson, *co-ordinator and author, Poverty and Inequality*

Bob Kelly, *assessment strategy and author, Study Guide to the Course Book*

Maureen Mackintosh, *author, Transitions*

Judith Mehta, *author, Transitions*

Stephen Peake, *author, Sustainability*

Sandrine Simon, *author, Sustainability*

Alan Thomas, *author and co-editor of the Course Book*

Richard Treves, *author, Sustainability*

David Wield, *critical reader*

Helen Yanacopulos, *co-ordinator and author, Technology and Knowledge*

BBC STAFF

Jenny Bardwell, *Series Producer July 2000–May 2001*

Gail Block, *Audio Producer*

Giselle Corbett, *Production Manager*

Phil Gauron, *Series Producer*

Julie Laing, *Series Personal Assistant*

Andrew Law, *Executive*

Jenny Morgan, *Freelance Director*

Claire Sandry, *Audio Producer*

Mercia Seminara, *Audio Producer*

SUPPORT STAFF

Carolyn Baxter, *Course Manager*

Sylvan Bentley, *Picture Researcher*

Philippa Broadbent, *Print Buying Controller*

Penny Brown, *QA Software Testing Assistant*

Daphne Cross, *Print Buying Co-ordinator*

Sue Dobson, *Web Designer*

Tony Duggan, *Learning Projects Manager*

Peta Jellis, *Course Manager July–November 2000*

Alison George, *Web Designer*

Richard Hoyle, *Graphic Designer*

Lori Johnston, *Editor*

Roy Lawrance, *Graphic Artist*

Cathy McNulty, *Course Secretary*

Katie Meade, *Rights Editor*

Lynda Oddy, *QA Software Testing Manager*

Pauline O'Dwyer, *Course Secretary*

Katharine Reedy, *Library Online Adviser*

Janice Robertson, *Editor*

John Taylor, *Copublishing Manager*

Mark Thomas, *Team Leader, Online Applications Web Team*

Pamela Wardell, *Editor*

EXTERNAL ASSESSOR

Dr K. Bezanson, *Institute of Development Studies, University of Sussex*

CONSULTANTS

Tim Allen, *author and co-editor of the Course Book*

Seife Ayele, *Poverty and Inequality*

Jo Beall, *Sustainability*

Flemming Christiaansen, *Transitions*

Ben Crow, *Sustainability*

Vandana Desai, *Displacement, and Study Guide to the Course Book*

Wendy Fisher, *Technology and Knowledge*

Leroi Henry, *Study Guide to the Course Book*

Ann Le Mare, *Preparing for Development*

Giles Mohan, *Displacement*

Paul Mosley, *Poverty and Inequality*

Njuguna N'gethe, *Study Guide to the Course Book*

Wendy Olsen, *Poverty and Inequality*

Ruth Pearson, *Poverty and Inequality*

Judith Scott, *Poverty and Inequality*

Laixiang Sun, *Transitions*

John Taylor, *Transitions*

David Turton, *Displacement*

Marc Wuyts, *Transitions*

CRITICAL READERS

Henry Bernstein, *Transitions*

Tenkai Bonger, *Sustainability*

Jessimen Chipika, *Poverty and Inequality*

Rachel Marcus, *Poverty and Inequality*

Martin Reynolds, *Sustainability*

Rafal Rohozinski, *Technology and Knowledge*

AbdouMaliq Simone, *Displacement*

WEB TESTERS

Alan Brown, Jackie Bush, Christine Cubbitt, Andrew Dakers, Sarah Downham, Alan Foster, Anna Mattarollo, Fahmida Muhit, Eric Needs, Wendy Shaffer, Nigel Shakespear, Phil Talman

U213
International Development: Challenges for a World in Transition

Course texts

Introduction to Transitions

Introduction to Poverty and Inequality

Introduction to Technology and Knowledge

Introduction to Displacement

Introduction to Sustainability

Transitions

Poverty and Inequality

Technology and Knowledge (web-based)

Displacement

Sustainability